A SHORT HISTORY OF CHEMISTRY

ISAAC ASIMOV is Associate Professor of Biochemistry at Boston University School of Medicine. He obtained his Ph.D. in chemistry from Columbia University in 1948 and has written voluminously on a number of branches of science and mathematics. Dr. Asimov is well known for his exceedingly popular science fiction (twenty-three volumes) and his remarkable ability to present the complex ideas of modern science in terms which are understandable to the non-scientist. In recent years he has grown particularly interested in the history of science, as is evidenced not only by this book but by his *A Short History of Biology* and *Asimov's Biographical Encyclopedia of Science and Technology*.

Professor Asimov has to his credit an impressive list of over sixty books in all. Among them are: *The Intelligent Man's Guide to Science, The Chemicals of Life, Life and Energy, The Genetic Code,* and *Inside the Atom.*

He lives in West Newton, Massachusetts with his wife and two children.

Books on Chemistry by Isaac Asimov

BIOCHEMISTRY AND HUMAN METABOLISM

THE CHEMICALS OF LIFE

CHEMISTRY AND HUMAN HEALTH

INSIDE THE ATOM

BUILDING BLOCKS OF THE UNIVERSE

THE WORLD OF CARBON

THE WORLD OF NITROGEN

THE INTELLIGENT MAN'S GUIDE TO SCIENCE

LIFE AND ENERGY

THE SEARCH FOR THE ELEMENTS

THE GENETIC CODE

ASIMOV'S BIOGRAPHICAL ENCYCLOPEDIA OF SCIENCE AND TECHNOLOGY

A SHORT HISTORY OF CHEMISTRY

A Short History of CHEMISTRY

BY

ISAAC ASIMOV

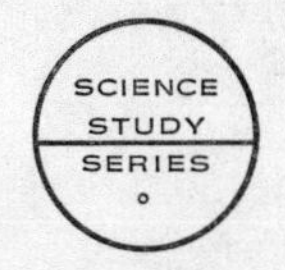

Published by Anchor Books
Doubleday & Company, Inc.
Garden City, New York
1965

Illustrations by Robert Yaffe

Library of Congress Catalog Card Number 65–10641

Printed in the United States of America
First Edition

To

Catherine and Sprague de Camp

who in twenty-five years have not aged a day

THE SCIENCE STUDY SERIES

The Science Study Series offers to students and to the general public the writing of distinguished authors on the most stirring and fundamental topics of science, from the smallest known particles to the whole universe. Some of the books tell of the role of science in the world of man, his technology and civilization. Others are biographical in nature, telling the fascinating stories of the great discoverers and their discoveries. All the authors have been selected both for expertness in the fields they discuss and for ability to communicate their special knowledge and their own views in an interesting way. The primary purpose of these books is to provide a survey within the grasp of the young student or the layman. Many of the books, it is hoped, will encourage the reader to make his own investigations of natural phenomena.

The Series, which now offers topics in all the sciences and their applications, had its beginning in a project to revise the secondary schools' physics curriculum. At the Massachusetts Institute of Technology during 1956 a group of physicists, high school teachers, journalists, apparatus designers, film producers, and other specialists organized the Physical Science Study Committee, now operating as part of Educational Services Incorporated, Watertown, Massachusetts. They pooled their knowledge and experience toward the design and creation of aids to the learning of physics. Initially their effort was supported by the National Science Foundation, which has continued to aid the program. The Ford Foundation, the Fund for the Advancement of Education, and the Alfred P. Sloan Foundation have also given support. The Committee has created a textbook, an extensive film series, a laboratory guide, especially designed apparatus, and a teacher's source book.

The Series is guided by a Board of Editors consisting of Bruce F. Kingsbury, Managing Editor; John H. Durston, General Editor; Paul F. Brandwein, the Conservation Foundation and Harcourt, Brace & World, Inc.; Samuel A. Goudsmit, Brookhaven National Laboratory; Philippe LeCorbeiller, Harvard University; and Gerard Piel, *Scientific American.*

CONTENTS

A SHORT HISTORY OF CHEMISTRY

CHAPTER 1

THE ANCIENTS

Fire and Stone

When early forms of man first began to use tools, they took nature as they found it. The thighbone of a large animal made a handy club; so did the branch torn from a tree. A rock was a convenient missile.

As millennia passed, men learned to shape rocks to give them cutting edges, or a gripping end. They learned to fit rocks into wooden handles, shaped for the purpose. Nevertheless, rock remained rock and wood remained wood.

However, there were times when the nature of substances did change. Lightning might set fire to a forest and the blackened or powdery ash was nothing like the wood that had existed before. Again, meat might decay and smell bad; fruit juice might grow sour on standing, or become oddly stimulating to drink.

It is such changes in the nature of substances (accompanied, as mankind eventually discovered, by fundamental changes in structure) that form the subject matter of the science we now call *chemistry*. Fundamental alteration in the nature and structure of a substance is a *chemical change*.

The opportunity to bring about chemical change deliberately for his own benefit arrived when man had mastered the art of starting and maintaining a fire. (This in historical terms was the "discovery of fire.") That art achieved, man became a practicing chemist, for he had to devise methods for causing wood, or other combustible material, to combine with air at a rate fast enough to produce sensible heat and light, as well as ashes, smoke, and vapors. Thus, wood had to be dried, some of it had to be powdered to tinder, temperatures had to be raised to the ignition point by friction or otherwise, and so on.

The heat produced by fire could be used to bring about further chemical changes. Food was cooked and its color, texture, and taste thereby altered. Clay could be baked into bricks and pottery. Eventually, ceramics, glazes, even forms of glass itself, could be formed.

The first materials used by man were those universals he found all about: wood, bone, hide, rock. Of these, rock is most durable and it is early man's stone implements that remain today as clearest reminders of that long-gone time. So we speak of the *Stone Age*.

Mankind was still in the Stone Age when, about 8000 B.C., a revolutionary change in food production was introduced in certain regions of what is now known as the Middle East. Previously, man had hunted food as any other animal might. Now he learned to domesticate animals and care for them as a reliable food supply. Even more important, he learned to cultivate plants. With animal husbandry and agriculture developed, a more stable and ample food supply was available, and the population increased. Agriculture required men to remain in one place, moreover, so that permanent habitations were built and cities developed. That evolution marks, literally, the beginning of civilization, for the word comes from the Latin term for "city."

For the first couple of thousands of years of this

earliest civilization, stone remained the characteristic tool material, although new techniques for handling it were devised. This *New Stone Age,* or *Neolithic Period,* was characterized by the careful polishing of stone. Pottery, too, reached an advanced stage of development. Slowly, the advances of the Neolithic period spread out from its Middle Eastern center. By 4000 B.C., for instance, the characteristics of the culture had appeared in western Europe. By then, however, the time was ripe for additional changes in the Middle East–in Egypt and in Sumeria (the region now occupied by the modern nation of Iraq).

Mankind began to learn to make use of comparatively rare materials. For the sake of the useful properties of the new materials, men learned to undergo all the inconveniences of tedious searching and processing. We call these materials *metals,* a word which in itself expresses this early change, for it is derived, possibly, from a Greek word meaning "to search for."

Metals

The first metals must have been found existing in the form of nuggets. They must have been pieces of *copper* or *gold,* for these are among the few metals occasionally found free in nature. The reddish color of copper or the yellowish color of gold must have caught the eye; and the metallic luster, which is so much more startling and beautiful than the flat, nondescript coloring of most stones, must then have held it. Undoubtedly the first use of metals was as ornaments, in whatever form the pieces had been found, much as colored pebbles or pearly sea shells might have so been used.

The advantage of metals over other pretty bits of

matter lay in this, however: Copper and gold are *malleable;* that is, they can be beaten flat without breaking. (Stone, so treated, would powder to dust; wood or bone would split and splinter.) This property undoubtedly was discovered by accident, but it could not have been long after the discovery when man's sense of artistry caused him to beat metal nuggets into intricate shapes that would enhance their beauty.

Workers in copper were bound to notice that this metal could easily be beaten into a sharper edge than could be produced on a tool of rock, and that some copper edges would hold their sharpness under conditions that would blunt a rock edge. Furthermore, a copper edge, once blunted, could be sharpened again more easily than a stone edge could. Only the rarity of copper prevented its widespread use for tools as well as ornament.

Copper became less rare, however, when it was discovered that it need not be found as copper. It could be manufactured out of stone. How this discovery was made, or where, or when, is not known exactly and may never be known.

We might guess that the discovery could have been made in a wood fire started in a bed of rocks that included some bluish ones. In the ashes, afterward, globules of gleaming copper might have been found. Perhaps this happened many times before it eventually dawned on someone that if the proper blue rocks were found, heating them in a wood fire would produce copper every time. The final discovery of this fact may have taken place about 4000 B.C. and it may have happened in the Sinai peninsula, just east of Egypt, or in the mountainous area east of Sumeria, in modern Iran. Perhaps it happened independently in both places.

In any case, copper became common enough to

be used for tools, at least in the advanced centers of civilization. A frying pan of copper found in an Egyptian tomb has been dated as 3200 B.C. By 3000 B.C. a particularly hard variety of copper was discovered. It was produced (by accident at first, no doubt) by the simultaneous heating of copper ores and tin ores. (See Figure 1.) The copper-tin *alloy* (the term used for a mixture of metals) is called *bronze,* and by 2000 B.C. bronze was common enough to be used for weapons and armor. Egyptian bronze tools have been found in the tomb of the Pharaoh Iteti, who reigned about 3000 B.C.

The most famous event of the *Bronze Age* was the Trojan War, in which bronze-clad, bronze-shielded warriors flung bronze-tipped spears at each other. An army without metal weapons couldn't possibly stand against the bronze warriors, and the metalworker of that day had something of the prestige of the nuclear physicist of today. The smith was a mighty man indeed, and was even accorded a place among the gods. Hephaestus, the lame god of the forge, was the divine smith of Greek mythology. And even today, it is no accident, that "Smith" or its equivalent is the most common name among the European peoples.

Lightning struck twice. The men of the Bronze Age knew of a metal even harder than bronze. This was *iron.* Unfortunately, it was too rare and precious to use, wholesale, for armor. At least, it seemed rare, for the only samples found in early times were bits of shattered meteorites, which are not common. Nor did there seem to be any way of obtaining iron out of rock.

The trouble was that iron was more firmly bound into its ore form than copper was. It required more intense heat to smelt iron than to smelt copper. A wood fire was insufficient for the purpose. The hot-

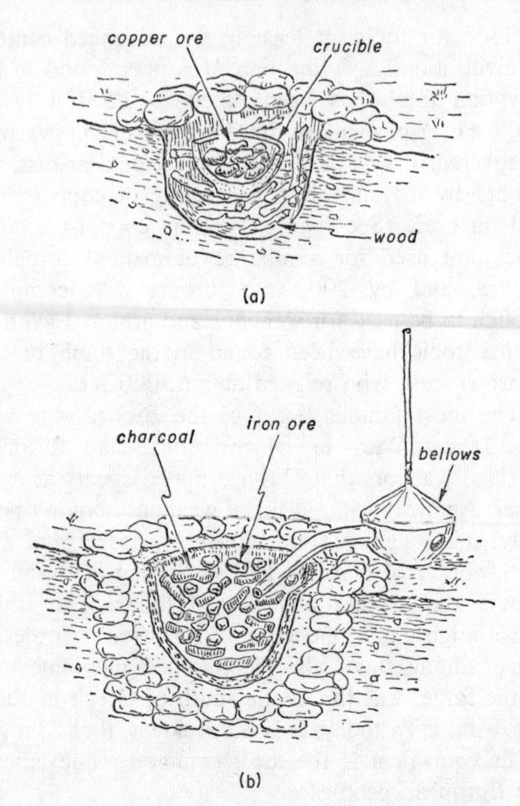

FIG. 1. Ancient smelters were designed to attain temperatures appropriate for reduction of different ores. In copper furnace (a) ore was melted in crucible over wood fire. Reduction of iron ore (b) required greater heat, obtained by lining furnace with charcoal and supplying oxygen with bellows.

ter charcoal fire was required, and even then only under conditions of good ventilation.

The secret of smelting iron was finally stumbled upon in eastern Asia Minor, perhaps as early as 1500 B.C. The Hittites, a people who built a great empire in Asia Minor, were the first to use iron routinely for tools. Letters dated about 1280 B.C., from a Hittite king to his viceroy in an iron-rich mountain region, make definite references to iron production.

Iron in pure form (*wrought iron*) is not very hard. However, an iron implement or weapon may pick up enough carbon from charcoal to form a surface layer of the iron-carbon alloy we call *steel.* This skin is harder than even the best bronze, and holds a sharper edge longer. It was this discovery of "steeling" in Hittite territory that was the crucial turning point in iron metallurgy. An army clad in hard iron and armed with hard iron was reasonably sure to defeat another army clad in and armed with bronze. Thus came the *Iron Age.*

The Dorians, a barbaric Greek tribe equipped with some iron weapons, invaded the Greek peninsula from the north in about 1100 B.C. and gradually overcame the more civilized but only bronze-armed Mycenaean Greeks who were already on the scene. Some Greeks penetrated to Canaan and brought iron weapons with them. These were the Philistines, who play so important a role in the early books of the Bible. Against them the Israelites were helpless until they obtained iron weapons for themselves under King Saul.

The first army to be equipped with good iron weapons in quantity was the Assyrian. By 900 B.C. superior armament helped them to build a mighty empire for themselves.

Before the dawn of the great days of Greece, then, the practical chemical arts had reached a good state of advancement. This was particularly true in Egypt, where there was great religious interest in methods for the embalming and preserving of the human body after death. Egyptians were expert not only in metallurgy but also in the production of pigments from the mineral world and juices and infusions from the plant world.[1]

According to one theory, the word *khemeia* derives from the Egyptians' name for their own land, *Kham.* (This name is also used in the Bible which, in the King James Version, becomes *Ham.*) *Khemeia* therefore might be "the Egyptian art."

A second theory, somewhat more favored at present, is that *khemeia* is derived from the Greek *khumos,* meaning the juice of a plant, so that *khemeia* may be considered as "the art of extracting juices." Or the juice referred to may even have been molten metal so that the word may mean "the art of metallurgy."

But whatever the source of *khemeia,* it is the ancestor of our word "chemistry."

Greek "Elements"

By 600 B.C., the volatile and intelligent Greeks were turning their attention to the nature of the universe and to the structure of the materials composing it. The Greek scholars or "philosophers" (lovers of wisdom) were concerned not so much with technology and with practical developments, as with the "why" of things. In short, they were the first we know of to deal with what we would now call *chemical theory.*

Such theory begins with Thales (c. 640–546 B.C.). There may have been Greeks before Thales, and even men before the Greeks, who thought deeply and well about the meaning behind changes in the

[1] The chemical arts were also developed in India and China. However, it is from Egypt, that the line of intellectual development in chemistry extends, and I will confine myself to that line.

nature of matter, but if so, their names and thoughts are lost to us.

Thales was a Greek philosopher, living in Miletus in Ionia, a region on the western Aegean coast of what is now the nation of Turkey. Thales must have asked himself the question: If one substance can be changed into another, as a bluish rock can be changed into red copper, what is the true nature of the substance? Is it rock or is it copper? Or are both something else entirely? Can any substance be changed (in a number of steps, perhaps) into any other substance, so that all substances are different aspects of one basic material?

To Thales the answer to the last question seemed yes, if only because thus a basic simplicity and order could be introduced into the universe. What remained, then, was to decide what that one basic material, or *element,* might be.[2]

Thales decided the element was water. Of all substances water seemed present in greatest quantities. Water surrounded the land; it permeated the atmosphere in vapor form; it trickled through the solid earth; life was impossible without it. He visualized the earth as a flat disk, topped by a semi-sphere of sky, and floating on an infinite ocean of water.

Thales' decision that there was an element of which all substances were formed met with considerable acceptance among later philosophers. His decision that the element was water was, however, disputed.

In the century after Thales, astronomical thinking came little by little to the conclusion that the sky was not a semi-sphere, but a complete one. The

[2] "Element" is a Latin word of uncertain origin. The Greeks did not use it, but it is so important to modern chemistry that there is no way of avoiding its use even with reference to Greek times.

earth, also spherical, was suspended at the center of the hollow sphere of the sky.

The Greeks did not accept the notion that a vacuum (complete emptiness) could exist, so they did not believe that the space between the suspended earth and the distant sky could contain nothing. Since the portion of the space between earth and sky that men could experience directly contained air, it seemed reasonable to suppose there was air all the way.

It may have been reasoning of this sort that led the Greek philosopher Anaximenes, also of Miletus, to conclude, about 570 B.C., that air was the element of the universe. He felt that toward the center of the universe it was compressed, forming the harder and denser varieties of substance such as water and earth. (See Figure 2.)

On the other hand, the philosopher Heraclitus (c. 540–c. 475 B.C.), from the neighboring town of Ephesus, took a different tack. If it was change that characterized the universe, then for the element one ought to seek a substance for which change was most characteristic. This substance, to him, seemed to be fire, ever shifting, ever changing. It was the fieriness in everything that made change so inevitable.[3]

In the time of Anaximenes, the Persians had conquered the Ionian coast. When an Ionian revolt failed, Persian rule became harsh, and under sup-

[3] It is easy to smile at these early notions, but actually these Greek guesses were quite profound. Suppose we substitute for "air," "water," "earth," and "fire," the very similar terms "gas," "liquid," "solid," and "energy." It is true that gases will condense to liquids if cooled and to solids if cooled still further. This is much like the situation Anaximenes imagined. And Heraclitus's views concerning fire are quite similar to our modern views concerning energy as both agent and consequence of chemical change.

FIG. 2. Alchemist's cosmology incorporated Aristotle's "four elements" with the terrestrial and celestial comparisons in which the same symbols were used for metals and the planets. This chart is after Robert Fludd (1574–1637), who turned his back on the scientific spirit of his age and pursued the occult.

pression the scientific tradition faded—not, however, before migrating Ionians had carried that tradition westward. Pythagoras of Samos (c. 582–c. 497 B.C.), native of an island off Ionia, left Samos in 529 B.C. and traveled to southern Italy, where his teachings left behind an influential body of thinking.

Eminent among those who adhered to the Pythagorean teachings was the Greek philosopher Empedocles (c. 490–c. 430 B.C.), a native of Sicily.

He, too, labored over the problem of the element out of which the universe was formed. There seemed no way of deciding among the proposals advanced by the Ionians, so Empedocles hit upon a compromise.

Why must there be but a single element? Why not four? There could be the fire of Heraclitus, the air of Anaximenes, the water of Thales, and the earth, which Empedocles himself added.

This doctrine of the *four elements* was accepted by the greatest of the Greek philosophers, Aristotle (384–322 B.C.). Aristotle did not consider the elements to be literally the substances named. That is, he did not imagine that the water we could touch and feel was actually the element "water"; it was merely the closest actual substance to it.

Aristotle viewed the elements as combinations of two pairs of opposed properties: hot and cold, dry and moist. He did not believe that one property could combine with its opposite, so in his scheme four possible combinations were left, each of which represented a different element. Hot-and-dry was fire, hot-and-moist was air, cold-and-dry was earth, and cold-and-moist was water.

He took one further step. Each element had its own innate set of properties. Thus it was the nature of earth to fall and of fire to rise. The heavenly bodies, however, had properties that seemed to differ from those of any substance on earth. Instead of either rising or falling, the heavenly bodies seemed to move in unchanging circles about the earth.

Aristotle therefore reasoned that the heavens had to be composed of a fifth element, which he called "ether" (from a word meaning "to glow," since the most characteristic property of the heavenly bodies was that they were luminous). As the heavens seemed unchanging, Aristotle considered the ether to be perfect, eternal, and incorruptible, quite different from the four imperfect elements of the earth itself.

The notion of the four elements held sway over the minds of men for two thousand years. Though now dead, as far as science is concerned, it still lives on in our common phrases. We speak of the "raging of the elements," for instance, when we wish to say that wind (air) and waves (water) are driven to fury by a storm. As for the "fifth element" (ether), the phrase becomes *quinta essentia* in Latin, and we still mark its Aristotelian perfection when we speak of the "quintessence" of anything, meaning that thing in its purest and most concentrated form.

Greek "Atoms"

Another major question arose among the Greek philosophers, one involving the divisibility of matter. The fragments of a stone, broken in two or even reduced to powder, were still stone, and each fragment could be further subdivided. Could such division and subdivision of matter proceed endlessly?

The Ionian Leucippus (c. 450 B.C.) seems to have been the first to question the perhaps natural assumption that any piece of matter, however small, could be divided into still smaller pieces. Leucippus maintained that eventually a piece would be obtained which was as small as it could be and was not subject to further division.

His disciple Democritus (c. 470–c. 380 B.C.), of the northern Aegean town of Abdera, continued this line of thought. He named these ultimately small particles *atomos,* meaning "indivisible," and we inherit this word as *atom*. The doctrine that matter is made up of ultimately small particles and is not indefinitely divisible is known as *atomism.*

It seemed to Democritus that the atoms of each element were distinct in size and shape and that it was this distinction that made each element different in properties. The actual substances we could see and handle were composed of mixtures of the atoms of the different elements, and one substance could be changed into another by altering the nature of the mixture.

All this sounds remarkably modern to us, but Democritus had no way of appealing to experiment for corroboration. (The Greek philosophers did not experiment but came to their conclusions by arguing from "first principles.")

For most philosophers, and especially for Aristotle, the notion of a piece of matter that could not be split into still smaller pieces seemed so paradoxical that they could not accept it. The atomistic view therefore remained unpopular and, for two thousand years after the time of Democritus, little heard of.

Atomism did not die out altogether, however. The Greek philosopher Epicurus (c. 342–270 B.C.) made atomism part of his way of thought, and Epicureanism won many adherents in the next few centuries. One of these adherents was the Roman poet Titus Lucretius Carus (c. 95–c. 55 B.C.), usually known simply as Lucretius. He expounded the atomist viewpoint of Democritus and Epicurus in a long poem entitled *De Rerum Natura* ("On the Nature of Things"). It is considered by many to be the finest didactic poem (one intended to teach) ever written.

In any case, while the works of Democritus and Epicurus perished so that only scraps and quotations remain, Lucretius's poem survived in full, and preserved the atomist view into modern times, when new scientific methods entered the struggle and brought it a final victory.

CHAPTER 2

ALCHEMY

Alexandria

In Aristotle's time, Alexander the Great of Macedon (a kingdom north of Greece) conquered the vast Persian Empire. Alexander's empire broke up after his death in 323 B.C., but Greeks and Macedonians remained in control of large areas of the Middle East. For the next few centuries (the "Hellenistic period") there was a fruitful mingling of cultures.

Ptolemy, one of Alexander's generals, established a kingdom in Egypt, with the city of Alexandria (founded by Alexander) as his capital. In Alexandria, Ptolemy and his son (Ptolemy II) established a temple to the Muses (the "Museum") which served as what we would today call a research institution and university. Attached to it, the greatest library of ancient times was built up.

Egyptian mastery of applied chemistry met and fused with Greek theory, but the fusion was not entirely to the good. Chemical knowledge in Egypt was intimately connected with the embalming of the dead and with religious ritual. To the Egyptians the ibis-headed god of wisdom, Thoth, was the source of all chemical knowledge. The Greeks, generally impressed by the superior knowledge of the Egyptians, identified Thoth with their own Hermes and accepted much of the mysticism.

The old Ionian philosophers had divorced religion and science. This new union in Egypt seriously interfered with further advance in knowledge.

Because the art of *khemeia* seemed so closely related to religion, the common people rather feared the practitioners as adepts of the secret arts and as partakers of dangerous knowledge. (The astrologer with his feared knowledge of the future, the chemist with his awesome ability to change substances, even the priest with his hidden secrets concerning the propitiation of the gods and with the ability to call down curses, served as models for folk-tales of magicians, wizards, and sorcerers.)

Those who were the object of these fears did not always resent them, but at times rather encouraged them as increasing their own sense of power, and perhaps their security as well. Who would care to offend a magician, after all?

This public respect or fear encouraged workers in *khemeia* to couch their writings in mysterious and obscure symbolism. The very obscurity added to the sense of secret knowledge and power.

As an example, there were seven heavenly bodies considered "planets" ("wanderers") because they were continually changing their position with reference to the starry background. There were also seven known metals: gold, silver, copper, iron, tin, lead, and mercury. (See Figure 2.) It seemed tempting to match them. There came a time when gold would be regularly referred to as "the Sun," silver as "the Moon," copper as "Venus" and so on. Chemical changes could then be referred to in mythological fashion.

There are still reminders of this time. One rather old-fashioned name for the chemical now called silver nitrate is "lunar caustic," a clear indication of the old connection of silver and the moon. The metal mercury gets its modern name from the planet Mercury. The true ancient name was *hydrargyrum* ("liquid silver"), and the old English word was the nearly identical "quicksilver."

This more or less deliberate obscurity served two unfortunate purposes. First, it retarded progress since each worker in the field was kept in ignorance, or at least in uncertainty, as to what others were doing, so that no man could profit by another's mistakes or learn from another's brilliance. Secondly, it made it possible for any quack and faker to present himself, provided he spoke obscurely enough, as a serious worker. The knave could not be distinguished from the scholar.

The first important worker in Greek-Egyptian *khemeia* that we know by name was Bolos of Mendes (c. 200 B.C.), a town in the Nile delta. In his writings, he used the name Democritus so that he is referred to as "Bolos-Democritus" or sometimes as the "pseudo-Democritus."

Bolos devoted himself to what became one of the great problems of *khemeia,* the changing of one metal into another and, particularly, the changing of lead or iron into gold (*transmutation*).

The four-element theory would make it seem that the various substances of the universe differed only in the nature of the elemental mixture. This hypothesis would be true whether one accepted the atomist view or not, since the elements could mix as atoms or as continuous substance. Indeed, there seemed reason to think that even the elements themselves were interchangeable. Water seemed to turn to air when it evaporated, and the air turned back to water when it rained. Wood, if heated, turned to fire and vapors (a form of air) and so on.

Why should any change, then, be considered impossible? Surely, it was only a matter of finding the proper technique. A reddish rock could be converted to gray iron through a technique that had not yet been discovered in the time of Achilles, who had to wear bronze armor. Why, then, should not gray iron be further converted to yellow gold by means of some technique that had not yet been discovered in the time of Alexander the Great?

Many chemists throughout the centuries have honestly striven to find the technique for producing gold. Some, however, undoubtedly found it much easier and far more profitable merely to pretend to find the technique and to trade on the power and reputation this gave them. This sort of fakery continued right on into modern times, but in this book we will not be concerned with this side of *khemeia.*

Bolos, in his writings, apparently gave the details of techniques of making gold, but this may not actually have represented fakery. It is possible to alloy copper with the metal zinc, for instance, to form *brass,* which has the yellow color of gold. It is quite likely that the preparation of a gold-colored metal would be the equivalent, to some of the ancient workers, of forming gold itself.

However, the art of *khemeia* went downhill during Roman times, along with a general decay of Greek learning. After A.D. 100 virtually nothing new was added, and there was a rising tendency to turn to ever-more mystical interpretations of the earlier writers.

About A.D. 300, for instance, an Egyptian-born writer, Zosimus, wrote an encyclopedia of twenty-eight books covering all the knowledge of *khemeia* that had accumulated in the previous five or six centuries, and there was very little of value in it. To be sure, one can find an occasional passage with something novel in it, like that seeming to refer to arsenic, and Zosimus seems to have described methods for forming lead acetate and to have known of the sweet taste of that poisonous compound. (It is called "sugar of lead" to this day.)

The final death blow came through fear. The Roman emperor Diocletian actually feared that *khemeia* might successfully produce cheap gold and destroy the shaky economy of the declining Empire. In Zosimus's time, he ordered writings on *khemeia* to be destroyed, which is one explanation of why little remains to us.

Another reason is that, with the rising tide of Christianity, "pagan learning" came into disfavor. The Alexandrian Museum and Library were badly damaged as a result of Christian riots after A.D. 400. The art of *khemeia,* with its close relationship to the ancient Egyptian religion, was particularly suspect and it virtually went underground.

In one respect, Greek learning left the Roman world altogether. Christianity had been broken up into sects, one of them called *Nestorians,* because they followed the teachings of a Syrian monk, Nestorius, who lived in the fifth century. The Nestorians were persecuted by the orthodox Christians of Constantinople, and a number of them fled eastward into Persia. There the Persian monarchs treated them with great kindness (possibly in the hope of using them against Rome).

The Nestorians brought Greek learning with them to Persia, including many books on alchemy. The peak of their power and influence came about A.D. 550.

The Arabs

In the seventh century, however, the Arabs came on the scene. Hitherto, they had been isolated on their desert peninsula, but now, stimulated by the new religion of Islam, founded by Mohammed, they burst outward in all directions. Their conquering armies took over vast areas of western Asia and northern Africa. In A.D. 641 they invaded Egypt, and after quick victories occupied the land, and over the next years they inflicted the same fate on all Persia.

In Persia, particularly, the Arabs met with what remained of the tradition of Greek science and were fascinated. A highly practical encounter may have encouraged this view, too. In A.D. 670, when they besieged Constantinople (the largest and strongest city in Christendom), they were driven off by "Greek fire," a chemical mixture that burned hotly with a fire that could not be put out with water and that destroyed the wooden ships of the Arabic fleet. According to tradition it was prepared by Callinicus, a practitioner of *khemeia* who had fled his native Egypt (or perhaps Syria) ahead of the Arabic armies.

In Arabic, *khemeia* became *al-kimiya,* the prefix *al* being their word for "the." The word was eventually adopted by Europeans as (in English) *alchemy,* and those who worked in the field were *alchemists.* The term alchemy is applied now to the entire course of chemical history from about 300 B.C. to A.D. 1600, a period of nearly two thousand years.

Between A.D. 300 and A.D. 1100 chemical history in Europe is virtually a blank. After A.D. 650 the preservation and extension of Greek-Egyptian alchemy were entirely in the hands of the Arabs and remained there for five centuries. Traces of this period remain in the number of chemical terms that are derived from Arabic: alembic, alkali, alcohol, carboy, naphtha, zircon, and others.

The best of Arabic alchemy came at the start of the period of their domination. Thus, the most capable and renowned of the Moslem alchemists was Jabir ibn-Hayyan (c. 760–c. 815), who was known to Europeans, centuries later, as "Geber." He lived at the time when the Arabic empire (under Haroun-al-Raschid of Arabian Nights fame) was at the height of its glory.

His writings were numerous and his style was relatively straightforward. (Many of the books bearing his name may have been written by later alchemists and attributed to him.) He described ammonium chloride and showed how to prepare white lead. He distilled vinegar to obtain strong acetic acid, which had been the strongest acid known to the ancients. He even prepared weak nitric acid which, potentially at least, was much stronger.

Jabir's greatest influence, however, lay in his studies in connection with the transmutation of metals. It seemed to him that mercury was the metal par excellence, since its liquid nature made it appear to have the least admixture of earthiness. Then sulfur seemed to possess the remarkable property of combustibility (and, further, possessed the yellow color of gold). It seemed to Jabir that the different metals were made up of different mixtures of mercury and sulfur, and it remained only to find some material that would facilitate the mixture of mercury and sulfur in the proper proportions to produce gold.

Ancient tradition held that such a transmutation-promoting substance was a dry powder. The Greeks called it *xerion* from their word for "dry." The Arabs changed this to *al-iksir* and to the Europeans it eventually became *elixir*. As a further testament to its supposed dry, earthy property, it was commonly called, in Europe, the *philosopher's stone*. (Remember that as late as 1800, a "philosopher" was what we now call a "scientist.")

The amazing elixir was bound to have other marvelous properties as well, and the notion arose that it was a cure for all diseases, and might very well confer immortality. Hence, one spoke of the *elixir of life,* and chemists who tired of the pursuit of gold could pursue immortality instead–also in vain.

In fact, for centuries afterward, alchemy flowed along two mainly parallel paths; a mineralogical one in which gold was the prime goal, and a medical one in which a panacea was.

Following Jabir, and with almost his skill and later reputation, was the Persian alchemist Al-Razi (c. 850–c. 925), known to Europeans later as "Rhazes." He, too, carefully described his work, preparing plaster of Paris, for instance, and describing the manner in which it could be used to form casts holding broken bones in place. He also studied and described metallic antimony. To mercury (which was volatile–that is, would form a vapor when heated) and to sulfur (which was inflammable) he added salt as a third principle in the composition of solids generally, for salt was neither volatile nor inflammable.

Al-Razi was more interested in medicine than Jabir had been, and this drift toward the medical aspects of alchemy continued with the Persian, Ibn-Sina (979–1037), who is much better known as Avicenna, the Latinized corruption of his name. Avicenna was, indeed, the most important physician between the time of the Roman Empire and that of the rise of modern science. He had learned enough from the failures of centuries to doubt whether the formation of gold from other metals was possible. In this, though, he was, and remained, an exception among alchemists.

Revival in Europe

Arabic science declined rapidly after Avicenna. Times were unsettled in the Islamic world and grew more unsettled still as a result of the invasions and military victories of the comparatively barbaric Turks and Mongols. The palm of scientific leadership left the Arabs after three centuries, never to return. It passed to western Europe.

The western Europeans had their first relatively peaceful and intimate contact with the Islamic world as a result of the Crusades. The First Crusade was launched in 1096, and western Christians conquered Jerusalem in 1099. For nearly two centuries afterward, a Christian realm existed on the Syrian coast, like a small island in the Moslem sea. There was a certain fusion of culture, and a drizzle of Christians returning to western Europe brought with them a certain appreciation of Arabic science. In that same period, the Christians in Spain were gradually retaking the territory that had been lost to Islam in the early eighth century. In so doing, they, and Christian Europe generally, gained a further notion of the brilliant Moorish civilization that had grown up in Spain.

Europeans learned that the Arabs possessed books of great learning which had been translated from the Greek originals–the works of Aristotle, for instance –as well as their own productions, such as the works of Avicenna.

Despite a certain reluctance to handle the works

of what seemed a deadly and inveterate enemy, the movement grew to translate these works into Latin to make them available to European scholars. The French scholar Gerbert (c. 940–1003), who became Pope Sylvester II in 999, was an early encourager of this movement.

The English scholar Robert of Chester (fl. 1140–50) was among the first to translate an Arabic work of alchemy into Latin, completing the task in 1144. Others followed, and the greatest of the translators was the Italian scholar Gerard of Cremona (c. 1114–87). He spent much of his life in Toledo, Spain, which had been taken by Christian forces in 1085. He translated ninety-two Arabic works, some of them extremely long.

Beginning about 1200, then, it became possible for European scholars to absorb the alchemical findings of the past and to attempt to advance beyond them, encountering, of course, as many or more blind alleys as broad avenues of progress.

The first important European alchemist was Albert of Bollstadt (c. 1200–80), better known as Albertus Magnus ("Albert the Great"). He studied the works of Aristotle intensively, and it was through him that Aristotelian philosophy grew so important to the scholarship of the later Middle Ages and of early modern times.

Albertus Magnus, in the course of reporting his alchemical experiments, described arsenic so clearly that he sometimes receives credit for the discovery of that substance although, in impure form at least, it was probably known to earlier alchemists.

A contemporary of Albertus Magnus was the English scholar and monk Roger Bacon (1214–92), who is best known today for his clearly expressed belief that in experimentation and in the application of mathematical techniques to science would lie the best hope for progress. He was right, but the world was not yet quite ready.

Bacon attempted to write a universal encyclopedia of knowledge and in his writings produced the earliest description of gunpowder. Bacon is sometimes thought of as the discoverer of gunpowder, but he wasn't; the real discoverer is unknown.

In time gunpowder helped to destroy the medieval order of society by giving armies a means to level castle walls, and the man on foot a chance to shoot down a horseman in armor. It was the earliest symbol of the technological proficiency that was to lead European armies to the conquest of the other continents during the five centuries from 1400 to 1900, a conquest that is being reversed only in our own lifetimes.

Alchemy in more mystic vein is to be found in works attributed to the Spanish scholars Arnold of Villanova (c. 1235–c. 1311) and Raymond Lully (1235–1315), though it is doubtful that they really were the authors. These writings lean heavily on transmutation, and Lully was even supposed (by tradition) to have manufactured gold for the wastrel Edward II of England.

The most important of the medieval alchemists, however, is not known by name, for he wrote under that of Geber, the Arabic alchemist of six centuries before. Nothing is known of this "false Geber" except that he was probably a Spaniard and wrote about 1300. He was the first to describe sulfuric acid, the most important single substance used by the chemical industries of today (after water, air, coal, and oil). He also described the formation of strong nitric acid. These acids were obtained from minerals, while the earlier known acids, such as the acetic acid of vinegar, came from the world of life.

This discovery of the strong *mineral acids* was

the most important chemical advance after that of the successful production of iron from its ore some three thousand years before. Many chemical reactions could be carried through, and many substances dissolved, by Europeans with the aid of the strong mineral acids, which the earlier Greeks and Arabs could not have brought about with vinegar, the strongest acid at their disposal.

The mineral acids were far more important to the welfare of mankind, in fact, than gold would have been even if that metal could have been produced by transmutation. Gold's value would have disappeared as soon as it was no longer rare, whereas the mineral acids are the more valuable the cheaper and more plentiful they become. Nevertheless, such is human nature that the mineral acids made no great impression, while gold continued to be sought for avidly.

But then, after a promising beginning, alchemy began to degenerate for the third time, as it had done first among the Greeks and then among the Arabs. The hunt for gold became the almost exclusive province of fakers, though great scholars even as late as the seventeenth century (Boyle and Newton are examples) could not resist trying their hand at it.

Once again, as under Diocletian a thousand years before, the study of alchemy was forbidden, as much in dread of the successful production of gold as in indignation over fakery. Pope John XXII declared such a ban in 1317, and honest alchemists, forced to work underground, became more obscure than ever, while chemical racketeering flourished as always.

The winds of change, however, were stirring more and more violently in Europe. The remnant of the Eastern Roman Empire (or "Byzantine Empire"), with its capital at Constantinople, was clearly in its last days. In 1204 it had been sacked brutally by western European Crusaders, and much of the record of Greek learning which, till then, had remained intact in that one city at least, was lost forever.

The Greeks recovered the city in 1261, but it was only a shadow of itself thereafter. Over the next two centuries Turkish armies of conquest drew inexorably closer to the city, and finally, in 1453, Constantinople fell and has remained Turkish ever since. Both before and after the fall, Greek scholars fled to western Europe, carrying with them such portions of their libraries as they could salvage. Only feeble remnants of Greek learning were made available to the West, but even they were immensely stimulating.

This was also the age of the great explorations, helped on by the discovery, in the thirteenth century, of the magnetic compass. The coast of Africa was explored and the continent was rounded in 1497. With India reached by sea and the world of Islam bypassed, Europe could trade directly with the Far East. Even more startling were the voyages of Christopher Columbus from 1492 to 1504 through which, it was soon discovered (though Columbus himself never admitted the fact), a new half of the world had been revealed.

So much unknown to the great Greek philosophers was being discovered by Europeans that the feeling must arise that the Greeks were not all-knowing supermen after all. The Europeans, having proved superior in navigation, might well prove superior in other respects as well. A certain psychological block was removed, and it became easier to question the findings of the ancients.

In this same "Age of Exploration" a German inventor, Johann Gutenberg (c. 1397–c. 1468) had devised the first practical printing press, making use of movable type that could be disassembled and put together to print any desired book. For the first time in history, it became possible to produce books cheaply and in quantity, without fear of errors in copying (though, of course, there might be errors in typesetting).

Unpopular views, thanks to printing, need not necessarily die out for lack of anyone to undertake the laborious effort of copying such a book. Thus, one of the early books to appear in printed form was Lucretius's poem (see page 14), and it spread the atomist view far and wide through Europe.

In the year 1543, two revolutionary books were published which, before the days of printing, might easily have been ignored by orthodox thinkers. Now, however, they made their way everywhere and could not be overlooked. One was a book by a Polish astronomer, Nicholas Copernicus (1473–1543), which held that the Earth was not the center of the universe as the great Greek astronomers had maintained, but that the Sun was. The other was a book by a Flemish anatomist, Andreas Vesalius (1514–64), which portrayed human anatomy with unprecedented accuracy. It was based on Vesalius's own observations, and refuted many of the beliefs that dated back to ancient Greek sources.

This simultaneous overthrowing of Greek astronomy and biology (though Greek views maintained their hold in some quarters for a century and more longer) marked the beginning of the "Scientific Revolution." This Revolution penetrated the alchemical world only slowly, but it made itself somewhat felt in both the mineralogical and medical aspects of the science.

The End of Alchemy

The new spirit appeared in the works of two contemporaries, both physicians, a German, Georg Bauer (1494–1555) and a Swiss, Theophrastus Bombastus von Hohenheim (1493–1541).

Bauer is better known as Agricola which, in Latin, means "farmer" (as Bauer does, in German). He became interested in mineralogy through its possible connection with medicines. In fact, the connection between medicine and minerals, and the combination of physician-mineralogist, was to be a prominent feature in the development of chemistry for the next two and a half centuries. Agricola's book *De Re Metallica* (*"Of Metallurgy"*) (see Figure 3) was published in 1556, and in it he summarized all the practical knowledge that could be gathered from the miners of his day.

This book, clearly written and with excellent illustrations of mining machinery, became popular at once and indeed remains a worthy classic of science even today.[1] The most important work on chemical technology before 1700, *De Re Metallica* established *mineralogy* as a science. (The most valuable book on metallurgy and applied chemistry generally, prior to Agricola, had been that of the monk Theophilus –possibly a Greek–who lived about A.D. 1000).

As for Von Hohenheim, he is better known by his self-chosen nickname of Paracelsus. This means "better than Celsus," Celsus having been a Roman writer on medical matters whose works had ap-

[1] It is interesting that the only English translation of Agricola's work, published in 1912, was made by former President Herbert Hoover, a mining engineer by profession, and his wife. With illustrations taken from the original, a handsome edition is available from Dover.

GEORGII AGRICOLAE
DE RE METALLICA LIBRI XII. QVI-
bus Officia, Inſtrumenta, Machinæ, ac omnia deniq; ad Metalli-
cam ſpectantia, non modo luculentiſſimè deſcribuntur, ſed & per
effigies, ſuis locis inſertas, adiunctis Latinis, Germanicisq; appel-
lationibus ita ob oculos ponuntur, ut clarius tradi non poſſint.

EIVSDEM

DE ANIMANTIBVS SVBTERRANEIS Liber, ab Autore re-
cognitus: cum Indicibus diuerſis, quicquid in opere tractatum eſt,
pulchrè demonſtrantibus.

BASILEAE M. D. LVI.

Cum Priuilegio Imperatoris in annos V.
& Galliarum Regis ad Sexennium.

FIG. 3. Title page of Agricola's *De Re Metallica.*

peared recently in a printed edition. They were the object of much and, to Paracelsus, mistaken idolatry.

Paracelsus, like Avicenna five centuries earlier (see page 22), represented a shift in alchemical interest from gold to medicine. The purpose of alchemy, Paracelsus maintained, was not to discover techniques for transmutation but to prepare medicines with which to treat disease. In earlier times plant preparations had been most often used for the purpose, but Paracelsus believed heartily in the efficacy of minerals as medicines.

Paracelsus was an alchemist of the old school despite his de-emphasis of transmutation. He accepted the four elements of the Greeks and the three principles (mercury, sulfur, and salt) of the Arabs. He sought unceasingly for the philosopher's stone in its function as the elixir of life, and even insisted he had found it. He also, in greater truth, discovered the metal *zinc,* and is sometimes considered its discoverer, although zinc, in the form of its ore and in alloy form with copper (brass), was known even in ancient times.

Paracelsus remained a figure of controversy for half a century after his death. His followers increased the content of mysticism in his views and reduced it to a mumbo-jumbo in some respects. This corruption met with disfavor in an era when alchemy was emerging more and more into an era of clarity and rationality.

For instance, the German alchemist Andreas Libau (c. 1540–1616), better known by the Latinized name Libavius, published *Alchemia* in 1597. This work was a summary of the medieval achievements of alchemy and might be considered the first chemical textbook worthy of the name, for he wrote clearly and without mysticism. In fact, he bitterly attacked the obscure theories of what he called the "Paracelsians," though he agreed with Paracelsus that the chief function of alchemy was to serve as handmaiden to medicine.

Libavius was the first to describe the preparation of hydrochloric acid, of tin tetrachloride, and of ammonium sulfate. He described also the preparation of aqua regia ("royal water"), a mixture of nitric acid and hydrochloric acid which receives its name from the fact that it can dissolve gold. He even suggested that mineral substances could be identified from the shape of the crystals produced when a solution is evaporated.

Nevertheless, he was certain that transmutation was possible and that the discovery of methods for making gold was an important end of chemical study.

A more specialized textbook was produced in 1604 by a German publisher named Johann Thölde (concerning whom nothing is otherwise known). He ascribed the book to a medieval monk named Basil Valentine, but it seems almost certain that the name was a pseudonym for himself. The book, entitled *The Triumphal Chariot of Antimony,* dealt with the medicinal uses of this metal and the compounds derived from it.

Still later came a German chemist, Johann Rudolf Glauber (1604–68), who discovered a method of forming hydrochloric acid by the action of sulfuric acid on ordinary salt. In the process he obtained a residue, sodium sulfate, which we still call "Glauber's salt" even today.

Glauber fastened onto this substance, studying it intensively, and noting its activity as a laxative. He called it "sal mirabile" ("wonderful salt"), and touted it as a cure-all, almost an elixir of life. Glauber went into the business of manufacturing this compound, as well as others which he considered of medical value. He made a successful living out of it, too. It was a less dramatic way of life than that of pursuing the manufacture of gold, but it was more useful and more profitable.

Even to those impervious to scientific rationale, the economic facts of life spoke loudly. There was too much that was useful and profitable in advancing knowledge of minerals and medicine to waste time in the interminable foolish dance after gold.

In the course of the seventeenth century, in fact, alchemy dwindled steadily in importance and in the eighteenth century became what we would today call chemistry.

CHAPTER 3

TRANSITION

Measurement

Yet, despite its advance, chemical knowledge in certain respects lagged behind other branches of science.

In astronomy the importance of quantitative measurements and of the application of mathematical techniques had been understood since ancient times. One reason was that the astronomical problems tackled by the ancients were relatively simple, and certain of them could be handled reasonably well even with plane geometry.

The application of mathematics and of careful measurement to physics was dramatized by the Italian scientist Galileo Galilei (1564–1642), who, in the 1590s, studied the behavior of falling bodies. The results of his work led, nearly a century later, to the important conclusions of the English scientist Isaac Newton (1642–1727). In his book *Principia Mathematica,* published in 1687, Newton introduced his *three laws of motion,* which served for over two centuries as the basis of the science of mechanics. In the same book Newton advanced his *theory of gravitation,* which also served for more than two centuries as an adequate explanation of the workings of the universe and holds true today within the limits of our personal observations and attainable velocities. In connection with this theory, he made use of the calculus, a new and powerful branch of mathematics which he himself had worked out.

The Scientific Revolution reached its climax in Newton. There was no question thereafter of deferring to the Greeks or to any of the ancients. Western Europe had far surpassed them and there was to be no more looking back.

But an equivalent change from mere qualitative description to careful quantitative measurement did not take place in chemistry for a full century after Newton's climactic work. In fact, while Newton was building the modern structure of astronomy and physics with a beauty and solidity that amazed the scientific world, he remained immersed in alchemy. He sought ardently throughout Europe for recipes whereby he might make gold by transmutation.

This persistence in the wrong approach was not entirely the fault of chemists. If they were slow to adopt the quantitative mathematical techniques of Galileo and Newton, it was because the material they dealt with was more difficult to represent in a fashion simple enough to be amenable to mathematical treatment.

Nevertheless, chemists made progress, and faint signs of a forthcoming chemical revolution were not wanting, even in Galileo's time. Such signs were present, for instance, in the work of a Flemish physician, Jan Baptista Van Helmont (1577–1644). He grew a tree in a measured quantity of soil, added water periodically, and carefully weighed the tree as it grew. Since he hoped to discover the source of the living tissue formed by the tree, he was applying measurement to a problem in chemistry, and in biology as well.

Until Van Helmont's time the only air-like substance known and studied was air itself, which seemed sufficiently distinctive and unlike other substances to serve as one of the elements of the Greeks (see page 11). To be sure, alchemists had frequently obtained "airs" and "vapors" in their experiments, but these were elusive substances that were hard to study and observe, and easy to ignore.

The mystery of these vapors was implicit in the very name given to liquids that vaporized easily. They were termed "spirits," a word originally meaning "breath" or "air," but carrying also an obvious sense of the mysterious and even of the supernatural. We still speak of "spirits of alcohol" and "spirits of turpentine." Alcohol is so much the oldest and best-known of the volatile liquids that "spirits" has come to refer to alcoholic liquors in particular.

Van Helmont was the first chemist to consider the vapors he produced and to study them. He found that they resembled air in physical appearance but not in all properties. In particular, he obtained vapors from burning wood that resembled air, but did not behave quite like air.

To Van Helmont these air-like substances, without fixed volume or fixed shape, were something akin to the Greek "chaos"; the original material, unshaped and unordered, out of which the Universe (according to Greek myth) was created. Van Helmont called the vapors by the name of "chaos," but spelled the word in accordance with its phonetic sound in Flemish, which made it *gas.* This word is still used today for all air-like substances.

The particular gas which Van Helmont obtained from burning wood and which he studied with particular care, he called "gas sylvestre" ("gas from wood"). It is what we call today *carbon dioxide.*

It was the study of gases, the simplest form of matter, that first lent itself to the techniques of careful measurement; it served as a highway to the world of modern chemistry.

Boyle's Law

Toward the end of Van Helmont's life, gases–air, in particular, since it was the most common gas–were attaining a new and dramatic importance. The Italian physicist Evangelista Torricelli (1608–47) was able to prove, in 1643, that air exerted pressure. He showed that air could support a column of mercury thirty inches high and, in so doing, he invented the barometer.

Gases at once became less mysterious. They were matter, possessing weight as did the more easily studied liquids and solids. They differed from liquids and solids chiefly in their much lower density.

The pressure exerted by the weight of the atmosphere was demonstrated in an astonishing manner by the German physicist Otto von Guericke (1602–86). He invented an air pump with which he could pull the air out of containers, so that the air pressure on the outside was no longer equalized by air pressure on the inside.

In 1654 Guericke prepared two metal hemispheres that fit together along a greased flange. When the hemispheres were put together and the air within was removed by the air pump, air pressure from without held the hemispheres together. Teams of horses attached to each of the hemispheres and whipped into straining their utmost in opposite directions, could not pull the hemispheres apart. When air was allowed to re-enter the joined hemispheres, however, they fell apart of themselves.

Demonstrations such as this roused great interest in the properties of air. In particular, the curiosity of an Irish chemist, Robert Boyle (1627–91), was roused. He devised an air pump of his own that was even better than Guericke's. Then having, so to speak, pulled air apart in sucking it out of a container, he went on to try the opposite procedure of compressing it—that is, of pushing it together.

In his experiments Boyle found that the volume of a sample of air varied with pressure according to a simple inverse relationship. (See Figure 4.) He discovered this by dropping mercury into a very long, specially constructed tube and trapping a sample of air in the short, closed end which was fitted with a stopcock. By adding more mercury to the long open end he could increase the pressure on the trapped air. If he added enough mercury to place the trapped air under doubled pressure (a doubled weight of mercury), the volume of the trapped air was halved. If pressure was tripled the volume was reduced to a third. On the other hand, if pressure was eased off the volume expanded. This relationship whereby volume decreased in proportion as pressure increased was first published in 1622 is still referred to as *Boyle's law.*

This was the first attempt to apply exact measurement to changes in a substance of particular interest to chemists.[1]

Boyle did not specify that temperature must be held constant if Boyle's law is to be valid. Probably he realized this and supposed it would be taken for granted. The French physicist Edme Mariotte (1630–1684), who discovered Boyle's law independently,

[1] It must be pointed out, though, that the change studied by Boyle was not a chemical one. Air, however it might be compressed or expanded, remains air. Such change in volume is a *physical change.* He was therefore involved in *physical chemistry,* the study of the physical changes of chemicals. This was not to come into its own for two centuries after the time of Boyle (see Chapter 9), but he laid the groundwork.

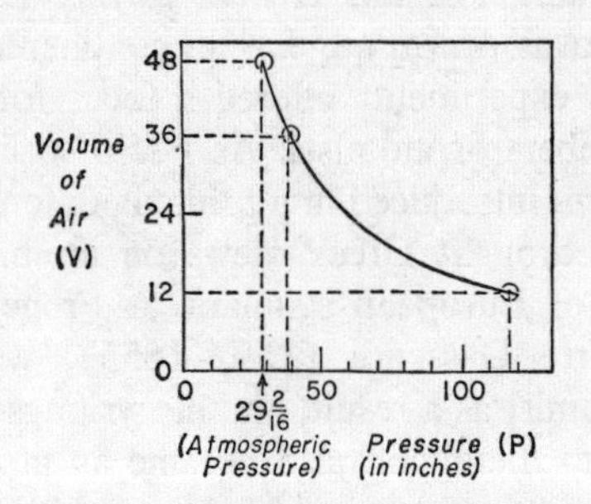

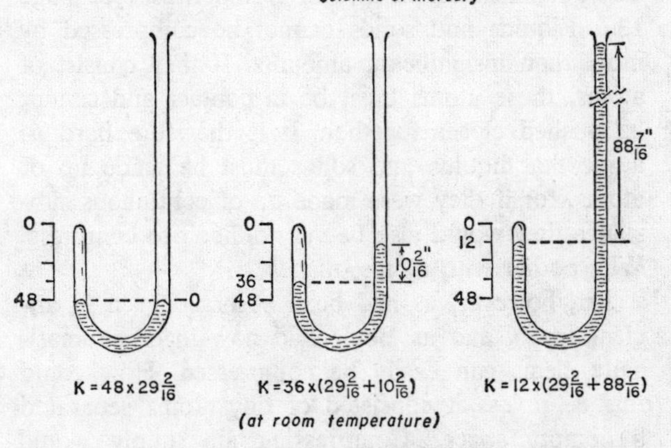

FIG. 4. Boyle's law, which established the inverse relationship of pressure and the volume of a gas at constant temperature, derived from the experiment illustrated below. Mercury dropped in long arm of tube drove the trapped air into short arm. Doubling the column of mercury halved the column of air. Relationship is plotted in the curve above, a section of one branch of the hyperbola.

about 1680, did specify that temperature must be held constant. For this reason, Boyle's law is often referred to as *Mariotte's law* in continental Europe.

Boyle's experiments offered a focus for the gathering numbers of atomists. As I said earlier, Lucretius's poem, introduced in a printed edition (see page 28), had brought Greek views on atomism to the attention of European scholars. A French philosopher, Pierre Gassendi (1592–1655), was a convinced atomist as a result, and his writings impressed Boyle, who thereupon also became an atomist.

As long as one concentrated on liquids and solids only, the evidence for atomism was no better in Boyle's time than in that of Democritus (see page 13). Liquids and solids cannot be compressed by more than insignificant amounts. If they consist of atoms, those atoms must be in contact and cannot be pushed closer together. It is therefore hard to argue that liquids and solids must be made up of atoms, for if they were made up of continuous substance they would also be very difficult to compress. Why bother with atoms, then?

Air, however, as had been observed even in ancient times, and as Boyle had now made dramatically clear, can easily be compressed. How could this be unless it consisted of tiny atoms separated by empty space? Compressing air simply would mean, from that point of view, the squeezing of empty space out of the volume, pushing the atoms closer together.

If this view of gases is accepted it becomes easier to believe that liquids and solids are composed of atoms, too. For instance, water evaporates. How can that be unless it disappears tiny bit by tiny bit, and what could be simpler, then, than to suppose that it turns into vapor atom by atom? If water is heated it boils and vapor is visibly formed. The water vapor has the physical properties of an air-like substance and therefore, it is natural to suppose, is composed of atoms. But if water is composed of atoms in its gaseous form, why not in its liquid form as well, and in its solid form of ice? And if this is true of water, why not of all matter?

Arguments of this sort were impressive, and for the first time since atoms were first imagined two thousand years before, atomism began to win numerous converts. Newton, for instance, became an atomist.

Nevertheless, atoms remained a misty concept. Nothing could be said about them except that if they were assumed to exist, it was easier to explain the behavior of gases. Another century and a half had to pass before atomism came into sharp focus.

The New View of Elements

Boyle's career marks the passing of the terms "alchemy" and "alchemist." Boyle dropped the first syllable of the term in writing a book, *The Sceptical Chymist,* published in 1661. From that time on, the science was *chemistry* and workers in the field were *chemists.*

Boyle was "sceptical" because he was no longer willing to accept, blindly, the ancient conclusions that had been deduced from first principles. In particular, Boyle was dissatisfied with ancient attempts to identify the elements of the universe by mere reasoning. Instead, he defined elements in a matter-of-fact, practical way. An element, it had been considered ever since Thales' time (see page 8), was one of the primal simple substances out of which the universe was composed. Well, then, a suspected element must be tested in order to see if it were really simple. If a substance could be broken into simpler substances it was not an element, but the simpler substances might be—until such time as chemists learned to break them down to still simpler substances.

Furthermore, if two substances were each an element, they might be intimately combined to form a third substance called a *compound*. If so, then that compound should lend itself to breakdown into the two original elements.

The term "element," in this view, had only a practical meaning. A substance such as quartz, for instance, could be considered an element until such time as experimental chemists discovered a way of converting it into two or more still simpler substances. In fact, no substance could ever be an element except in a provisional sense, according to this view, since one could never be certain when advancing knowledge might make it possible to devise a method for breaking down a supposed element into still simpler substances.

It was not until the coming of the twentieth century that the nature of elements could be defined in a non-provisional sense (see page 218).

The mere fact that Boyle wanted an experimental approach in defining elements (an approach that was adopted eventually) does not mean that he knew what the different elements were. It might have turned out, after all, that the experimental approach would indeed have proved Greek elements of fire, air, water, and earth to be elements.

Boyle was convinced, for instance, of the validity of the alchemical viewpoint that the various metals were not elements and that one metal could be converted into another. In 1689, he urged the British government to repeal the law against the alchemical manufacture of gold (they, too, feared the upset to the economy) because he felt that by forming gold out of base metal, chemists could help to prove the atomic view of matter.

But Boyle was wrong there; the metals did prove to be elements. In fact, nine substances which we now recognize as elements had been known to the ancients: the seven metals (gold, silver, copper, iron, tin, lead, and mercury) and two non-metals (carbon and sulfur). In addition, there were four substances now recognized as elements that had become familiar to the medieval alchemists: arsenic, antimony, bismuth, and zinc.

Boyle, himself, came within a hair of being the discoverer of a new element. In 1680 he prepared *phosphorus* from urine. Some five to ten years before that, however, the feat had been accomplished by a German chemist, Hennig Brand (?–c. 1692). Brand is sometimes called the "last of the alchemists," and, indeed, his discovery came while he was searching for the philosopher's stone which he thought he would find in (of all places) urine. Brand was the first man to discover an element that had not been known, in at least some form, before the development of modern science.

Phlogiston

The seventeenth-century discoveries concerning air pressure and the unusual feat that one could perform by producing a vacuum and allowing air pressure to work, had important results. It occurred to several people that a vacuum might be formed without the use of an air pump.

Suppose you boiled water and filled a chamber with steam, then cooled the chamber with cold water on the outside. The steam within the chamber would condense into a few drops of water, and a vacuum would exist in its place. If one of the walls of the chamber were movable, air pressure on the other side would then drive that wall into the chamber.

The movable wall could be pushed outward again if more steam were formed and allowed to enter the chamber, and then be pushed inward again if the steam were once more condensed. If you imagine the movable wall to be part of a piston, you can see that the piston will move in and out and that this in-and-out motion could be used to run a pump, for instance.

By 1700, such a *steam engine* had actually been produced by an English engineer, Thomas Savery (c. 1650–1715). It was a dangerous device because it used steam under high pressure at a time when high-pressure steam could not be safely controlled. However, another Englishman, Thomas Newcomen (1663–1729), working in partnership with Savery, devised a steam engine that would work on low-pressure steam. (See Figure 5.) The device was improved and made really practical, toward the end of the eighteenth century, by the Scottish engineer James Watt (1736–1819).

The result of these labors was that, for the first time, mankind was no longer dependent upon its own muscles or upon the muscles of animals. Nor was man dependent upon the hit-or-miss force of the wind, or upon the spottily located energy of running water. Instead, he had a source of energy he could call upon at any time and in any place merely by boiling water over a wood or coal fire. This was the chief factor marking the start of the "Industrial Revolution."

The increasing interest from 1650 onward in the possibility of turning fire to new uses and, by way of the steam engine, making it do the heavy work of the world, brought to chemists a new awareness of

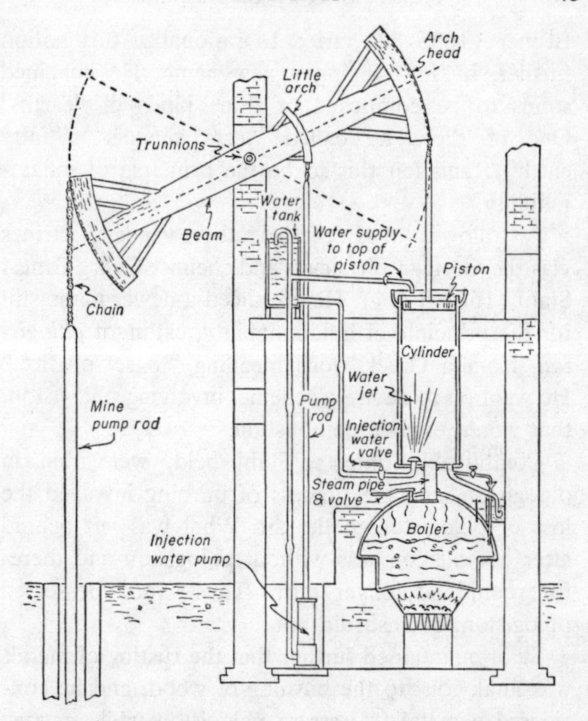

FIG. 5. Newcomen pumping engine operated under atmospheric pressure. Water sprayed into cylinder condensed steam, creating a vacuum. Piston descended into vacuum, to be returned to top of stroke by a new injection of steam.

fire. Why do some things burn and others not? What is the nature of combustion?

By old Greek notions something which could burn contained within itself the element of fire, and this something was released under the proper conditions. Alchemical notions were similar, except that a combustible was thought of as containing the principle of "sulfur" (though not necessarily actual sulfur).

In 1669, a German chemist, Johann Joachim

Becher (1635–82), tried to rationalize this notion further, by introducing a new name. He imagined solids to be composed of three kinds of "earth." One of these he called "terra pinguis" ("fatty earth"), and felt this to be the principle of inflammability.

A follower of Becher's rather vague doctrines was the German physician and chemist Georg Ernest Stahl (1660–1734). He advanced a newer name still for the principle of inflammability, calling it *phlogiston,* from a Greek word meaning "to set on fire." He went on to devise a scheme, involving phlogiston, that would explain combustion.

Combustible objects, Stahl held, were rich in phlogiston, and the process of burning involved the loss of phlogiston to the air. What was left behind after combustion was without phlogiston and therefore could no longer burn. Thus, wood possessed phlogiston, but ash did not.

Stahl maintained further that the rusting of metals was analogous to the burning of wood, and he considered a metal to possess phlogiston while its rust (or "calx") did not. This was an important insight, which made it possible to advance a reasonable explanation of the conversion of rocky ores into metals —the first great chemical discovery of civilized man. The explanation consisted of this: A rocky ore, poor in phlogiston, is heated with charcoal, which is very rich in phlogiston. Phlogiston passes from the charcoal into the ore, so that the phlogiston-rich charcoal is turned into phlogiston-poor ash, while the phlogiston-poor ore is turned into phlogiston-rich metal.

Air itself was considered by Stahl to be only indirectly useful to combustion, for it served only as a carrier, holding the phlogiston as it left the wood or metal and passing it on to something else (if something else were available).

Stahl's phlogiston theory met with opposition at first, notably from a Dutch physician, Hermann Boerhaave (1668–1738), who argued that ordinary combustion and rusting could not be different versions of the same phenomenon.

To be sure, there is the presence of flame in one case and not in the other, but to Stahl the explanation was that in the combustion of substances, such as wood, phlogiston left so rapidly that its passage heated its surroundings and became visible as flame. In rusting the loss of phlogiston was slower and no flame appeared.

Despite Boerhaave's opposition, then, the phlogiston theory gained popularity throughout the eighteenth century. By 1780 it was almost universally accepted by chemists, since it seemed to explain so much so neatly.

Yet a difficulty remained that neither Stahl nor any of his followers could explain. Most combustible objects, such as wood, paper, and fat, seemed largely to disappear upon burning. The remaining soot or ash was much lighter than the original substance. This is to be expected, perhaps, since phlogiston had left that original substance.

However, when metals rusted, they also lost phlogiston, according to Stahl's theory, yet the rust was heavier than the original metal (a fact which had been noted by alchemists as early as 1490). Could phlogiston have negative weight, then, so that a substance that lost it was heavier than before, as some eighteenth-century chemists tried to maintain? If so, why did wood lose weight in burning? Were there two kinds of phlogiston, one with weight and one with negative weight?

This unanswered problem was not as serious in

the eighteenth century as it seems to us today. We are used to measuring phenomena accurately, and an unexplained change in weight would disturb us. The eighteenth-century chemists, however, had not yet accepted the importance of accurate measurements, and they could shrug off the change in weight. As long as the phlogiston theory could explain changes in appearance and properties, changes in weight, they felt, could be ignored.

CHAPTER 4

THE GASES

Carbon Dioxide and Nitrogen

The explanation of the puzzling changes in weight during combustion was to be found, of course, in the gases that appeared or disappeared while the products were forming. Despite the slowly growing knowledge of gases since the time of Van Helmont, a century earlier (see page 35), there was still no attempt in Stahl's day to take them into account in any way except to note their existence. In thinking of weight changes in combustion, the investigators had eyes only for solids and liquids. Ash was lighter than wood, but what about the vapors given off by the burning wood? Not considered. Rust was heavier than metal, but had rust gained anything from the air? Not considered.

Before this deficiency could be corrected, chemists had to grow more familiar with gases. The terrors of a substance that seemed so hard to hold, confine, and study had to be overcome.

The English chemist Stephen Hales (1677–1761) made a step in the right direction, in the early eighteenth century, when he collected gases over water. The vapors formed as a result of a chemical reaction could be led, through a tube, into a jar of water that had been upended in a basin of water. The gas bubbled upward into the jar, displacing the water and forcing it out through the open bottom. In the end, Hales had obtained a jar of the particular gas or gases formed in the reaction.

He himself did not distinguish between the different gases he had prepared and trapped, or study their properties. The mere fact that he had devised a simple technique for trapping them, however, was of first-rate importance.

Another important step forward was taken by a Scottish chemist, Joseph Black (1728–99). The thesis that earned him a medical degree in 1754 dealt with a chemical problem (this was the era when mineralogy and medicine were closely intertwined), and he published his findings in 1756. What Black did was to heat, strongly, the mineral limestone (calcium carbonate). This carbonate decomposed, giving off a gas and leaving behind lime (calcium oxide). The gas given off could be made to recombine with calcium oxide to form calcium carbonate again. The gas itself (carbon dioxide) was identical with Van Helmont's "gas sylvestre" (see page 36), but Black called it "fixed air" because it could be combined ("fixed") in such a way as to form part of a solid substance.

Black's findings were important for a number of reasons. First, he showed that carbon dioxide could be formed by the heating of a mineral, as well as by the burning of wood, so that an important connection was made between the animate and inanimate realm.

Again, he showed that gaseous substances were not merely given off by solids and liquids, but could actually combine with them to produce chemical changes. This discovery made gases that much less mysterious and presented them, rather, as a variety of matter possessing additional properties in common (chemically at least) with the more familiar solids and liquids.

Still further, Black showed that when calcium oxide was allowed to stand in air, it turned slowly to calcium carbonate. From this, he deduced (correctly) that there were small quantities of carbon dioxide in the atmosphere. Here was the first clear indication that air was not a simple substance and, therefore, despite Greek notions, that it was not an element by Boyle's definition. It consisted of a mixture of at least two distinct substances, ordinary air and carbon dioxide.

In studying the effect of heat on calcium carbonate, Black measured the loss of weight involved. He also measured the quantity of calcium carbonate that would neutralize a given quantity of acid. This was a giant step toward the application of quantitative measurement to chemical changes, a method of analysis that was soon to come to full maturity with Lavoisier.

In studying the properties of carbon dioxide, Black found that a candle would not burn in it. A candle burning in a closed container of ordinary air would go out eventually, and the air that was left would then no longer support a flame. This behavior certainly seemed reasonable, since the burning candle had formed carbon dioxide. But when the carbon dioxide in the trapped air was absorbed by chemicals, some air remained unabsorbed. This air that was left and that was not carbon dioxide would still not support a flame.

Black turned this problem over to one of his students, the Scottish chemist Daniel Rutherford (1749–1819). Rutherford kept a mouse in a confined quantity of air till it died. He then burned a candle in what was left until the candle went out. He then burned phosphorus in what was left after that, until the phosphorus would no longer burn. Next, the air was passed through a solution that had the ability to absorb carbon dioxide. The air remaining now would not support combustion; a mouse would not live in it and a candle would not burn.

Rutherford reported this experiment in 1772. Since Rutherford and Black were both convinced of the validity of the phlogiston theory, they tried to explain their result in terms of this theory. As mice breathed and as candles and phosphorus burned, phlogiston was given off and entered the air, along with the carbon dioxide that was formed. When the carbon dioxide was later absorbed, the air left behind still contained much phlogiston. In fact, it contained so much phlogiston as to be saturated with it; it would accept no more. That was why objects no longer burned in it.

On this reasoning Rutherford called the gas he had isolated "phlogisticated air." Nowadays, we call it *nitrogen*, and give Rutherford the credit for its discovery.

Hydrogen and Oxygen

Two other English chemists, both upholders of the phlogiston theory, further advanced the studies of gases at this time.

One of these was Henry Cavendish (1731–1810). He was a wealthy eccentric who did research in a number of fields, but kept to himself and did not always publish the results of his work. Fortunately, he did publish the results of his work with gases.

Cavendish was particularly interested in a gas that was formed when acids reacted with certain metals. This gas had been isolated before by Boyle and Hales and perhaps others, but Cavendish, in 1766, was the first to investigate its properties systematically. He usually gets the credit, therefore, for its discovery. Eventually the gas was named *hydrogen.*

Cavendish was the first to measure the weight of particular volumes of different gases so that he might determine the density of each gas. He found hydrogen to be unusually light, with only one-fourteenth the density of air. (It is still the least dense gas known.) It had a second unusual property for, unlike carbon dioxide and air itself, it was easily inflammable. Cavendish, considering its extreme lightness and inflammability, speculated on the possibility that he had actually isolated phlogiston itself.

The second chemist was Joseph Priestley (1733–1804). He was a Unitarian minister who was deeply concerned with chemistry as a hobby. In the late 1760s, he took over a pastorate in Leeds, England, next door to which, as it happened, was a brewery. Fermenting grain produces carbon dioxide, which Priestley thus could obtain in quantity for experiments.

In collecting carbon dioxide over water, he found that some of it dissolved and lent the water a pleasantly tart taste. This is what we call "seltzer" or "soda water" today. Since it requires only added flavoring and sugar to produce "soda pop," Priestley may be viewed as the father of the modern soft-drink industry.

Priestley went on to study other gases in the early 1770s. At the time only three gases were known as distinct individuals: air itself, the carbon dioxide of Van Helmont and Black, and the hydrogen of Cavendish. Rutherford was about to add nitrogen as a fourth. Priestley, however, proceeded to isolate and study a number of additional gases.

His experience with carbon dioxide having showed him that gases could be soluble in water, and so lost to his experiments, he tried collecting them instead over mercury. By this method he was able to collect and study such gases as nitrogen oxide, ammonia, hydrogen chloride, and sulfur dioxide (to give them their modern names), all of which are too soluble in water to survive passage through it.

In 1774, the use of mercury in his work with gases was the occasion of Priestley's most important discovery. Mercury, when heated in air, will form a brick-red "calx" (which we now call mercuric oxide). Priestley put some of this calx in a test tube and heated it with a lens that concentrated sunlight upon it. The calx broke down to mercury again, for the metal appeared as shining globules in the upper portion of the test tube. In addition, the decomposing calx gave off a gas with most unusual properties. Combustibles burned more brilliantly and rapidly in this gas than in air. A smoldering splint of wood thrust into a container of the gas burst into flame.

Priestley tried to explain this phenomenon in terms of the phlogiston theory. Since objects burned so easily in this gas, they must be capable of giving off phlogiston with unusual ease. Why should this be so, unless the gas was a sample of air from which the usual content of phlogiston had been drained, so that it accepted a new supply with special eagerness? Priestley therefore called his new gas "dephlogisticated air." (A few years later, however, it was renamed *oxygen*, the name we use today.)

Priestley's "dephlogisticated air" did, indeed, seem to be the opposite of Rutherford's "phlogisticated air." Mice died in the latter, but were particularly active and frisky in the former. Priestley tried breathing some "dephlogisticated air" and found himself feeling "light and easy."

But both Rutherford and Priestley had been anticipated by a Swedish chemist, Karl Wilhelm Scheele (1742–86), one of a group of chemists who brought Sweden to the forefront of science in the eighteenth century.

One of these Swedes, George Brandt (1694–1768), had studied, about 1730, a bluish mineral that resembled copper ore but which, to the exasperation of the miners, yielded no copper when put through the usual treatment. The miners thought it was ore that had been bewitched by the earth-spirits they called "kobolds." Brandt was able to show that the mineral contained no copper, but contained, rather, a new metal (resembling iron in its chemical properties) which he named *cobalt* after the earth-spirits.

In 1751, Axel Fredric Cronstedt (1722–65) discovered the very similar metal, *nickel;* Johann Gottlieb Gahn (1745–1818) isolated *manganese* in 1774, and Peter Jacob Hjelm (1746–1813) isolated *molybdenum* in 1782.

The discovery of these new elements by Swedes demonstrated the strides mineralogy was making in that nation. Cronstedt, for instance, introduced the blowpipe into the study of minerals. (See Figure 6.) This was a long, narrowing tube which, when blown into at the wide end, produced a concentrated jet of air at the narrow end. This jet, directed into a flame, increased its heat.

When the heated flame impinged on minerals, information concerning the nature and composition of the mineral could be gathered from the color of the flame, the nature of the vapors formed, the oxides or metallic substances left behind, and so on. The blowpipe remained a key tool in *chemical analysis* for a century.

Enough knowledge was gained about minerals through new techniques such as that of the blow-

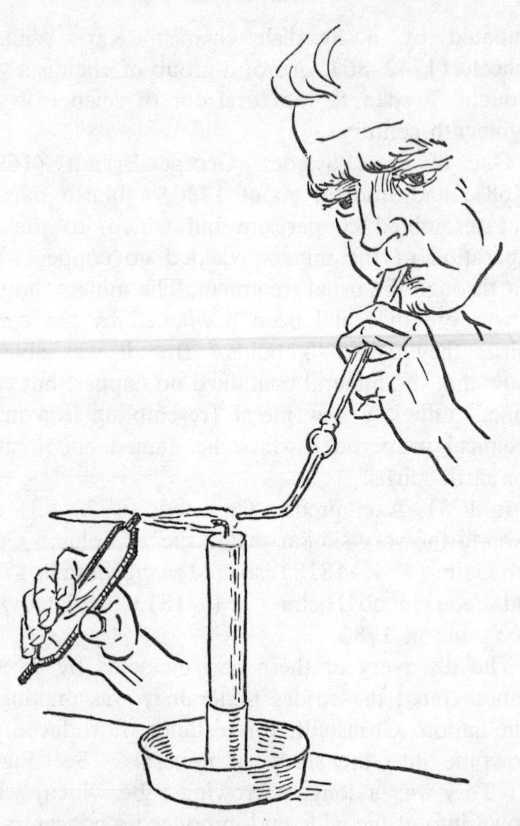

FIG. 6. Blowpipe, introduced into the laboratory by the Swedish chemist Cronstedt (1722–65), was a key tool in analysis for more than a century and is used still. Air jet from pipe increases and directs flame's heat.

pipe, that Cronstedt felt justified in suggesting that minerals be classified not only according to their appearance but also according to their chemical structure. A book detailing this new form of classification was published in 1758.

This work was carried further by another Swedish

mineralogist, Torbern Olof Bergman (1735–84). Bergman evolved a theory to explain why one substance reacted with a second but not with a third. He supposed the existence of "affinities" (that is, attractions) between substances in varying degree. He prepared elaborate tables listing various affinities, and these tables were very influential during his lifetime and for a few decades afterward.

Scheele, who began life as an apothecary's apprentice, attracted the attention of Bergman, who befriended and sponsored him. Scheele discovered a variety of acids, including tartaric acid, citric acid, benzoic acid, malic acid, oxalic acid, and gallic acid in the plant kingdom; lactic acid and uric acid in the animal; and molybdic acid and arsenious acid in the mineral.

He prepared and investigated three highly poisonous gases: hydrogen fluoride, hydrogen sulfide, and hydrogen cyanide. (His early death is supposed to have been the result of slow poisoning by the chemicals he worked with, which he would routinely taste.)

Scheele was involved in the discovery of most of the elements for which credit is given to his Swedish friends. Most important of all, he prepared oxygen and nitrogen in 1771 and 1772. He prepared oxygen by heating a number of substances that held it loosely, including the mercuric oxide used by Priestley, a couple of years afterward.

Scheele described his experiments carefully but, through the negligence of his publisher, the descriptions did not appear in print until 1777. By that time the work of Rutherford and Priestley had appeared, and they gained the credit for the discoveries.

The Triumph of Measurement

As the eighteenth century drew toward its close, the numerous important discoveries made in connection with gases needed to be drawn together into some over-all theory. The man to do that was on the scene. He was the French chemist Antoine Laurent Lavoisier (1743–94).

From the very beginning of his chemical researches, Lavoisier recognized the importance of accurate measurement. Thus, his first important work, in 1764, lay in an investigation of the composition of the mineral gypsum. This he heated to drive off the water content, and then measured the quantity of water so given off. He joined the company of those who, like Black and Cavendish, were applying measurement to chemical change. Lavoisier, however, went about it more systematically, and used it as a tool with which to break down the ancient theories which were no longer useful and which merely encumbered, if they did not stifle, chemical advance.

There were still some, for instance, who, even in 1770, clung to the old Greek notion of the elements and held that transmutation was possible because water could be turned to earth on long heating. This supposition seemed reasonable (even to Lavoisier at first) for water, heated for a period of many days in a glass container, did develop a solid sediment.

Lavoisier decided to test this alleged transmutation by more than eyesight. For 101 days he boiled water in a device that condensed the water vapor and returned it to the flask so that no substance was permanently lost in the course of the experiment. And, of course, he did not forget to measure. He weighed both water and vessel before and after the long period of boiling.

The sediment did appear, but the water did not change its weight during the boiling. Therefore, the sediment could not have been formed out of the water. However, the flask itself, once the sediment had been scraped away, proved to have lost weight, a loss just equal to the weight of the sediment. In other words, the sediment was not water turning to earth, it was material from the glass, slowly etched away by the hot water and precipitated in solid fragments. Here was a clear example where measurement could lead to a demonstration of reasonable fact, while the testimony of the eyes alone led to a false conclusion.

Lavoisier was interested in combustion, first, because it was the great chemical problem of the eighteenth century, and second, because one of his early triumphs had been an essay in the 1760s on improved methods for street-lighting. He began in 1772, when he clubbed together with other chemists to buy a diamond which he then heated in a closed vessel until it disappeared. Carbon dioxide was formed, the first clear demonstration that diamond was a form of carbon and therefore closely related to, of all things, coal.

He went on to heat metals such as tin and lead in closed containers, with a limited supply of air. Both metals formed a layer of "calx" on the surface up to a certain point and then rusted no further. The phlogistonists would say that the air had now absorbed all the phlogiston from the metal that it could hold. As was well known, however, the calx weighed more than the metal itself, and yet when Lavoisier weighed the entire vessel (metal, calx, air, and all) after the heating, it weighed precisely the same as it had before the heating.

It followed from this result that if the metal had gained weight on being partially turned to a calx, then something else in the vessel must have lost an equivalent amount of weight. That something else, it seemed, would have to be air. If that were so, then a partial vacuum must exist in the vessel. Sure enough, when Lavoisier opened the vessel, air rushed in. Once that had happened, the vessel and its contents proved to have gained in weight.

Lavoisier had thus shown that the conversion of a metal into a calx was not the result of a loss of mysterious phlogiston, but was the gain of something very material, a portion of the air.

Now it was possible for him to advance a new explanation for the formation of metals from ores. Ores were a combination of metal and gas. When an ore was heated with charcoal, the charcoal took the gas from the metal, forming carbon dioxide and leaving the metal behind.

Thus, whereas Stahl said the process of smelting involved the passage of phlogiston from charcoal to ore, Lavoisier said it involved the passage of gas from ore to charcoal. But were not these two explanations the same thing, with one equal to the other backwards? Was there any reason to prefer Lavoisier's explanation to Stahl's? Yes, there was, for by Lavoisier's theory of gas-transfer, one could explain the weight changes that resulted in combustion.

A calx was heavier than the metal from which it formed, by the weight of the added portion of the air. Wood also burned through addition of air to its substance, but it did not appear to gain weight, because the new substance formed (carbon dioxide) was itself a gas and vanished into the atmosphere. The ash left behind was lighter than the original wood. If wood were burned in a closed vessel, the gases formed in the process would remain in the system, and then it could be shown that the ash, plus the vapors formed, plus what was left of the air, would retain the original weight of wood plus air.

In fact, it seemed to Lavoisier in the course of his experiments that if all the substances taking part in a chemical reaction and all the products formed were taken into consideration, there would never be a change in weight (or, to use the more precise term of the physicists, a change in mass).

Lavoisier maintained, therefore, that mass was never created or destroyed, but was merely shifted from one substance to another. This concept is the *law of conservation of mass,* which served as the very cornerstone of nineteenth-century chemistry.[1]

Lavoisier's achievements through the use of measurement were so great, as you can see, that chemists accepted the principle of measurement wholeheartedly from his time forward.

Combustion

Lavoisier was not yet entirely satisfied. Air combined with metal to form a calx and with wood to form gases, but not all the air combined in this fashion. Only about a fifth of it did. Why was this?

Priestley, discoverer of "dephlogisticated air" (see page 54), visited Paris in 1774 and described his discoveries to Lavoisier. Lavoisier saw the significance at once and in 1775 published his views.

Air is not a simple substance, he said, but is a mixture of two gases in a 1 to 4 proportion. One-fifth of the air was Priestley's "dephlogisticated air"

[1] With the opening of the twentieth century, this law was shown to be incomplete, but the correction made necessary by the increased sophistication of twentieth-century science is an extremely small one and can be neglected in the ordinary reactions occurring in the chemical laboratory.

(though Lavoisier unfortunately neglected to give Priestley due credit). It was this portion of the air, and this portion only, that combined with burning or rusting materials, that was transferred from ore to charcoal, and that was essential to life.

It was Lavoisier who gave this gas its name, oxygen. This was from Greek words meaning "acid producer," Lavoisier having the idea that oxygen was a necessary component of all acids. In this, as it turned out, he was mistaken (see page 90).

The remaining four-fifths of the air, which could not support combustion or life (Rutherford's "phlogisticated air"), was a separate gas altogether. Lavoisier called it "azote" (from Greek words meaning "no life") but later the term nitrogen replaced it. This word means "forming niter," since niter, a common mineral, was found to contain nitrogen as part of its substance.

Lavoisier was convinced that life was supported by some process that was akin to combustion,[2] for we breathe in air rich in oxygen and low in carbon dioxide, but breathe out air that is lower in oxygen and considerably richer in carbon dioxide. He and a co-worker, Pierre Simon de Laplace (1749–1827) —who was later to become a famous astronomer— attempted to measure the oxygen taken in and the carbon dioxide given off by animals. The results were puzzling, for some of the oxygen that was inhaled did not appear in the carbon dioxide exhaled.

In 1783 Cavendish was still working with his inflammable gas (see page 52). He burned some of it and studied the consequences. He found that the vapors produced by the burning condensed to form a liquid that, on investigation, proved to be nothing more nor less than water.

[2] In this, he proved to be right.

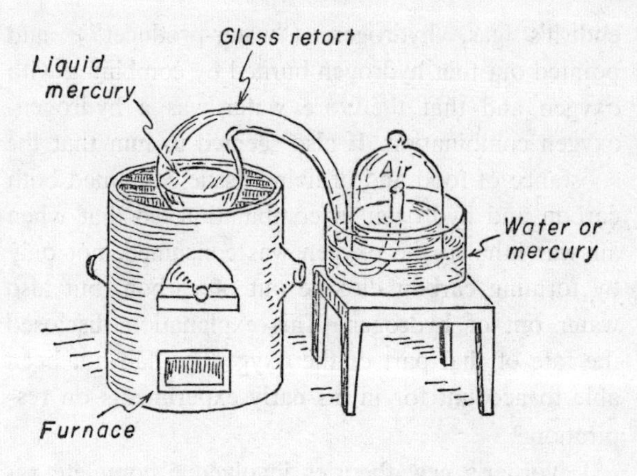

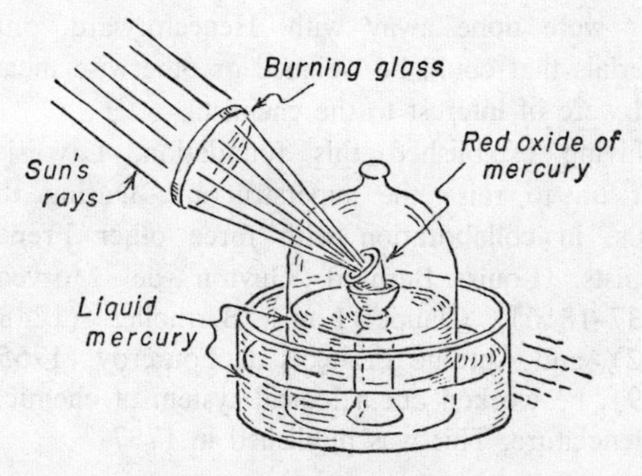

FIG. 7. Lavoisier's experiments were illustrated in *Elements of Chemistry* with drawings by Madame Lavoisier. (From Great Books edition)

This was a crucially important experiment. In the first place, it was another hard blow at the Greek theory of the elements, for it showed that water was not a simple substance but was the sole product of the combination of two gases.

Lavoisier, hearing of the experiment, named Cavendish's gas, hydrogen ("water-producer") and pointed out that hydrogen burned by combining with oxygen and that therefore water was a hydrogen-oxygen combination. It also seemed to him that the substance of food and of living tissue contained both carbon and hydrogen in combination, so that when air was inhaled the oxygen was consumed, not only by forming carbon dioxide out of carbon, but also water out of hydrogen. This explanation disclosed the fate of that part of the oxygen he had not been able to account for in his early experiments on respiration.[3]

Lavoisier's new theories involved a complete rationalization of chemistry. All mysterious "principles" were done away with. Henceforward, only materials that could be weighed or otherwise measured were of interest to the chemist.

Having established this foundation, Lavoisier went on to raise the superstructure. During the 1780s, in collaboration with three other French chemists, Louis Bernard Guyton de Morveau (1737–1816), Claude Louis Berthollet (1748–1822), and Antoine François de Fourcroy (1755–1809), he worked out a logical system of chemical nomenclature. This was published in 1787.

[3] In his theories Lavoisier had been anticipated by a Russian chemist, Mikhail Vasilievich Lomonosov (1711–65) who, in 1756, nearly twenty years before Lavoisier's work on combustion, had rejected the phlogiston theory and had suggested that objects combined with a portion of the air on burning. Unfortunately, he published in Russian, and the chemists of western Europe, including Lavoisier, were unaware of his work. Lomonosov also had startlingly modern views on atoms and on heat, which were fifty to a hundred years ahead of his time. He was a most remarkable man who suffered under the misfortune of having been born in eastern Europe at a time when scientific advance was concentrated in western Europe.

No longer was chemistry to be a farrago of names as in alchemical days (see page 17), each writer using his own system and puzzling everyone else. There was to be a recognized system that all were to use; a system based on logical principles, so that one could tell from the name of a compound the elements that made it up. For instance, calcium oxide was made up of calcium and oxygen; sodium chloride of sodium and chlorine; hydrogen sulfide of hydrogen and sulfur; and so on.

A careful system of prefixes and suffixes was set up so that one could tell something about the proportions in which the different elements were present. Thus, carbon dioxide contained more oxygen than did carbon monoxide. Again, potassium chlorate contained more oxygen than potassium chlorite, while potassium perchlorate contained still more oxygen, while potassium chloride contained no oxygen at all.

In 1789, Lavoisier published a book (*Elementary Treatise on Chemistry*) which served to supply the world with a unified picture of chemical knowledge on the basis of his new theories and nomenclature. It was the first modern chemical textbook.

Among other things, the book included a list of all the elements known up to that time (or, rather, all the substances which Lavoisier judged to be elements on the basis of Boyle's criterion–that they could not be broken down to simpler substances). (See Figure 8.) It is a credit to Lavoisier's judgment that in the thirty-three items he listed, only two were completely wrong. These were "light" and "caloric" (heat), which, as was to become plain in the decades after Lavoisier, were not material substances at all, but forms of energy.

Table of Simple Substances Belonging to All the Kingdoms of Nature, Which May Be Considered as the Elements of Bodies

New Names	Old Names
Light	Light
Caloric	Heat Principle or element of heat Fire. Igneous fluid Matter of fire and of heat
Oxygen	Dephlogisticated air Empyreal air Vital air, or base of vital air
Azote	Phlogisticated air or gas Mephitis, or its base
Hydrogen	Inflammable air or gas, or the base of inflammable air

Oxidable and Acidifiable Simple Substances Not Metallic

New Names	Old Names
Sulfur Phosphorus Charcoal	The same names
Muriatic radical Fluoric radical Boracic radical	Still unknown

FIG. 8. List of elements compiled by Lavoisier appeared in his *Elements of Chemistry*. (Translation taken from the Great Books Foundation's edition.)

Table of Simple Substances, Continued
Oxidable and Acidifiable Simple Metallic Bodies

New Names		Old Names
Antimony	Regulus of	Antimony
Arsenic		Arsenic
Bismuth		Bismuth
Cobalt		Cobalt
Copper		Copper
Gold		Gold
Iron		Iron
Lead		Lead
Manganese		Manganese
Mercury		Mercury
Molybdenum		Molybdenum
Nickel		Nickel
Platinum		Platinum
Silver		Silver
Tin		Tin
Tungsten		Tungsten
Zinc		Zinc

Salifiable Simple Earthy Substances

New Names	Old Names
Lime	Chalk, calcareous earth Quicklime
Magnesia	Magnesia, base of Epsom salt Calcined or caustic magnesia
Barytes	Barytes, or heavy earth
Argill	Clay, earth of alum
Silex	Siliceous or vitrifiable earth

FIG. 8 (continued)

Of the remaining thirty-one items, some were indeed elements according to present views. These included the substances, such as gold and copper, that had been known to the ancients, as well as others, such as oxygen and molybdenum, that had been discovered only in the years just prior to the publication of Lavoisier's book. Eight of the substances listed (lime and magnesia, for example) are no longer accepted as elements because, since Lavoisier's time, they have been broken down into simpler substances. In every case, however, one of those simple substances proved to be a new element.

There was some opposition to the new views of Lavoisier (views that have been retained to the present time), notably from some diehard phlogistonists, Priestley among them. Others, however, accepted the new chemistry enthusiastically. Bergman, in Sweden, was one of these. In Germany, the chemist Martin Heinrich Klaproth (1743–1817) was an early convert. His acceptance of Lavoisier's views was important for, since Stahl had been a German, there was a tendency among Germans to cling to phlogiston as a patriotic gesture. (Klaproth made his name later as a discoverer of elements. He discovered *uranium* and *zirconium,* in 1789.)

In the same year that Lavoisier's textbook was published, the French Revolution broke out, degenerating quickly into the wild excesses of the Terror. Lavoisier, unfortunately, was connected with a tax-collecting organization that the revolutionists considered a vicious tool of the hated monarchy. They executed, by guillotine, all its officers whom they could seize. One of them was Lavoisier.

In 1794, then, this man, one of the greatest chemists who ever lived, was needlessly and uselessly killed in the prime of life. "It required only a moment to sever that head, and perhaps a century will not be sufficient to produce another like it," said Joseph Lagrange, the great mathematician. Lavoisier is universally remembered today as "the father of modern chemistry."

CHAPTER 5

ATOMS

Proust's Law

Lavoisier's successes stimulated chemists to search out and explore other areas in which accurate measurements might illuminate the study of chemical reactions. The acids comprised one such area.

Acids form a natural group sharing a number of properties. They tend to be chemically active, reacting with metals such as zinc, tin, or iron, dissolving them and producing hydrogen. They taste sour (if dilute enough or weak enough to be tasted with impunity), cause certain dyes to change colors in certain ways, and so on.

Opposed to the acids is another group of substances called *bases*. (Strong bases are termed *alkalis*.) These are also chemically active, taste bitter, change dye colors in a fashion opposite to that induced by acids, and so on. In particular, solutions of acids will neutralize solutions of bases. In other words, if acids and bases are mixed in proper proportions, then the mixture will show the property of neither acids nor bases. The mixture will be, instead, a solution of a *salt,* which, in general, is a much milder chemical than either an acid or a base. Thus, a solution of the strong and caustic acid, hydrochloric acid, if mixed with the proper amount of the strong and caustic alkali, sodium hydroxide, will become a solution of sodium chloride, ordinary table salt.

The German chemist Jeremias Benjamin Richter (1762–1807) turned his attention to these neutralization reactions, and measured the exact amounts of different acids that were required to neutralize a given quantity of a particular base, and vice versa. By careful measurements he found that fixed and definite amounts were required. There wasn't the leeway that a cook might count on in the kitchen, where a bit more or less of some ingredient is not terribly important. Instead, there was such a thing as an *equivalent weight:* a fixed weight of one chemical reacted with a fixed weight of another chemical. Richter published his work in 1792.

Two French chemists were then engaged in strenuous battle over whether this sort of definiteness existed not only in acid-base neutralization but throughout chemistry. To put it fundamentally, if a particular compound were made up of two elements (or three or four), were those two elements (or three or four) always present in this compound in the same, fixed proportions? Or would these proportions vary, depending on the exact method of preparing the compound? Berthollet, one of those who collaborated with Lavoisier in establishing modern chemical terminology (see page 64), thought the latter. According to Berthollet's view, if a compound consisted of elements *x* and *y,* then it would contain a more than average quantity of *x,* if it were prepared while using *x* in large excess.

Opposed to Berthollet's view was the opinion of Joseph Louis Proust (1754–1826), who did his work in Spain, safe (for a time) from the upheavals of the French Revolution. Using painstakingly careful analysis, Proust showed, in 1799, that copper carbonate, for instance, contained definite proportions by weight of copper, carbon, and oxygen, no matter how it was prepared in the laboratory or how it was isolated from natural sources. The preparation was always 5.3 parts of copper to 4 of oxygen to 1 of carbon.

Proust went on to show that a similar situation was true for a number of other compounds, and formulated the generalization that all compounds contained elements in certain definite proportions and in no other combinations, regardless of the conditions under which they were produced. This is called the *law of definite proportion* or, sometimes, *Proust's law*. (Proust also showed that Berthollet, in presenting evidence that certain compounds varied in composition according to the method of preparation, was misled through inaccurate analyses and through the use of products he had insufficiently purified.)

During the first few years of the nineteenth century, it became quite clear that Proust was right. Other chemists verified the law of definite proportions, and it became a cornerstone of chemistry.[1]

From the moment Proust's law was announced, serious thoughts concerning it were forced into the chemical view.

After all, why should the law of definite proportions hold true? Why should a certain compound be made up always of 4 parts x and 1 part y, let us say, and never of 4.1 parts x or 3.9 parts x to 1 part y. If matter were continuous, this would be hard to understand. Why could not elements be mixed in slightly varying proportions?

But what if matter was atomistic in nature? Sup-

[1] It is true that some substances can vary, within limits, in their elemental constitution. These are special cases. The simple compounds which engaged the attention of the chemists of 1800 held firmly to the law of definite proportions.

pose a compound was formed when one atom of *x* joined with one atom of *y* and not otherwise. (Such a combination of atoms eventually came to be called a *molecule,* from a Latin word meaning "a small mass.") Suppose, next, that each atom of *x* happened to weigh four times as much as each atom of *y*. The compound would then have to consist of exactly 4 parts of *x* to 1 part of *y*.

In order to vary those proportions, an atom of *y* would have to be united with slightly more or slightly less than one atom of *x*. Since an atom, ever since the time of Democritus, had been viewed as being an indivisible portion of matter, it was unreasonable to expect that a small piece might be chipped off an atom, or that a sliver of a second atom might be added to it.

In other words, if matter consisted of atoms, then the law of definite proportions followed as a natural consequence. Furthermore, from the fact that the law of definite proportions was an observed fact, one could deduce that atoms were indeed indivisible objects.

Dalton's Theory

An English chemist, John Dalton (1766–1844), went through this chain of reasoning. In this, he was greatly aided by a discovery he made. Two elements, he found, might, after all, combine in more than one set of proportions, but in so doing they exhibited a wide variation of combining proportions and a different compound was formed for each variation. (See Figure 9.)

As a simple example, consider the elements carbon and oxygen. Measurement shows that 3 parts of carbon (by weight) will combine with 8 parts of oxygen to form carbon dioxide. However, 3 parts

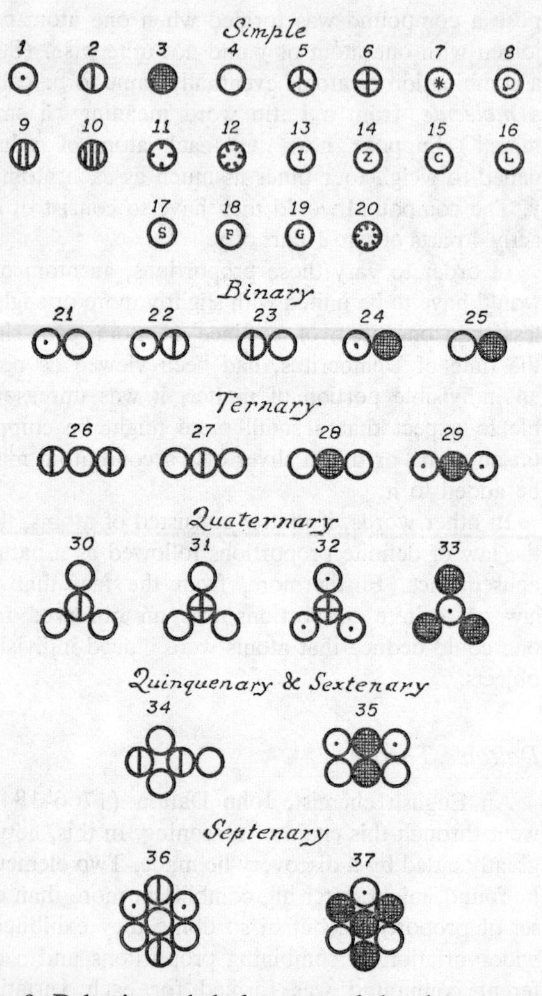

FIG. 9. Dalton's symbols for some of the elements and compounds. Among them, hydrogen (1); carbon (3); oxygen (4); copper (15); silver (17); gold (19); water (21). He went wrong on water, giving it as HO instead of H_2O, but his formulas for carbon monoxide (25) and carbon dioxide (28) were correct.

of carbon and 4 parts of oxygen make up carbon monoxide. In such a case, the differing quantities of oxygen that combine with a fixed amount of carbon are found to be related in the form of small whole numbers. The 8 parts present in carbon dioxide is exactly twice that of the 4 parts present in carbon monoxide.

This is the law of *multiple proportions.* Dalton, after observing its existence in a number of reactions, advanced it in 1803.

The law of multiple proportions fits in neatly with atomistic notions. Suppose, for instance, that atoms of oxygen are uniformly 1-1/3 times as heavy as atoms of carbon. If carbon monoxide is formed through the combination of one atom of carbon with one atom of oxygen, the compound must consist of 3 parts by weight of carbon to 4 parts of oxygen.

Then, if carbon dioxide is formed of one atom of carbon and two atoms of oxygen, the proportion must naturally consist of 3 parts of carbon to 8 of oxygen.

The relationship in simple multiples would reflect the existence of compounds varying in makeup by whole atoms. Surely, if matter did indeed consist of tiny, indivisible atoms, these would be just the variations in makeup you would expect to find, and the law of multiple proportions makes sense.

When Dalton put forward his new version of the atomic theory based on the laws of definite proportion and of multiple proportion, in 1803, he acknowledged the debt to Democritus by keeping the term "atom" for the small particles that made up matter.

In 1808, he published *A New System of Chemical Philosophy,* in which his atomic theory was discussed in greater detail. In that year, too, his law of multiple proportions was verified by the investigations of another English chemist, William Hyde Wollaston (1766–1828). Wollaston lent his influential weight to the atomic theory in consequence, and Dalton's view in due course won general acceptance.

The atomic theory, by the way, was a death blow (if any were needed) to belief in the possibility of transmutation on alchemical terms. All evidence seemed to point to the possibility that the different metals each consisted of a separate type of atom. Since atoms were taken generally to be indivisible and unchangeable (see, however, Prout's hypothesis, page 84), one could not expect to change a lead atom to a gold atom in any circumstances. Lead, therefore, could not be transmuted to gold.[2]

Dalton's atoms were, of course, far too small to be seen even under a microscope; direct observation was out of the question. Indirect measurements, however, could yield information as to their relative weights.

For instance, 1 part (by weight) of hydrogen combined with 8 parts of oxygen to form water. If one assumed that a molecule of water consisted of one atom of hydrogen and one atom of oxygen, then it would follow that the oxygen atom was eight times as heavy as the hydrogen atom. If it was decided to set the weight of the hydrogen atom arbitrarily equal to 1, then the weight of the oxygen atom on that scale would be 8.

Again, if 1 part of hydrogen combines with 5 parts of nitrogen in forming ammonia, and it is assumed that the ammonia molecule is made up of one

[2] A century after Dalton's time this view had to be modified. One atom could, after all, be changed to another (see page 243). The methods used to achieve this, however, were such as no alchemist ever imagined or could have performed.

atom of hydrogen and one of nitrogen, it would follow that the nitrogen atom would have a weight of 5.

Reasoning after this fashion, Dalton set up the first table of *atomic weights.* This table, although perhaps his most important single contribution, proved to be quite wrong in many entries. The chief flaw lay in Dalton's insistence that in general molecules were formed by the pairing of a single atom of one element with a single atom of another. He varied from this position only when absolutely necessary.

Evidence piled up, however, that indicated such a one-to-one combination was not necessarily the rule at all. The disagreement showed up in connection with water, in particular, even before Dalton had advanced his atomic theory.

Here, for the first time, the force of electricity invades the world of chemistry.

Knowledge of electricity dates back to the ancient Greeks, who found that when amber is rubbed, it gains the power to attract light objects.

Centuries later, the English physicist William Gilbert (1540–1603) was able to show that it was not amber alone that acted so, but that a number of other substances as well gained an attracting power when rubbed. About 1600, he suggested that substances of this sort be called "electrics," from the Greek word for amber.

As a result, a substance that gains such a power, through rubbing or otherwise, is said to carry an *electric charge,* or to contain *electricity.*

The French chemist Charles François de Cisternay du Fay (1698–1739) discovered, in 1733, that there were two kinds of electric charge: one that could be put on glass ("vitreous electricity") and one that could be put on amber ("resinous electricity"). A substance carrying one kind of charge attracted another substance carrying the other, but two substances bearing the same kind of charge repelled each other.

Benjamin Franklin (1706–90), who was the first great American scientist as well as a great statesman and diplomat, suggested, in the 1740s, that there was a single electrical fluid. When a substance contained a greater than normal quantity of electric fluid, it possessed one kind of electric charge; when it contained a less than normal quantity, it possessed the other kind.

Franklin guessed it was the glass that contained the greater than normal quantity of electric fluid, so he said it carried a *positive charge*. The resin, he said, carried a *negative charge*. Franklin's terms have been used ever since, although the usage leads to a concept of current flow opposite to what now is known to be the fact.

The Italian physicist Alessandro Volta (1745–1827) introduced something new. He found, in 1800, that two metals (separated by solutions capable of conducting an electric charge) could be so arranged that new charge was created as fast as the old charge was carried off along a conducting wire. He had invented the first *electric battery* and produced an *electric current*.

Such an electric current is maintained by the chemical reaction involving the two metals and the solution between. Volta's work gave the first clear indication that chemical reactions had something to do with electricity, a suggestion that was not to be developed completely for another century. If a chemical reaction could produce an electric current, it did not seem to be too farfetched to suppose that an electric current could reverse matters and produce a chemical reaction.

Indeed, within six weeks of Volta's first description of his work, two English chemists, William

Nicholson (1753–1815) and Anthony Carlisle (1768–1840), demonstrated the reverse action. They ran an electric current through water and found that bubbles of gas began to appear at the electricity-conducting strips of metal which they had inserted in the water. The gas appearing at one strip was hydrogen and that appearing at the other was oxygen.

In effect, Nicholson and Carlisle had decomposed water into hydrogen and oxygen, such decomposition by an electric current being called *electrolysis*. They had achieved the reverse of Cavendish's experiment (see page 62), in which hydrogen and oxygen had been combined to form water.

When the hydrogen and oxygen were trapped in separate vessels as they bubbled off, it turned out that just twice as large a volume of hydrogen was formed as of oxygen. The hydrogen was the lighter in weight, to be sure, but the larger volume indicated that there might be more atoms of hydrogen than of oxygen in the water molecule.

Since there was just twice as large a volume of hydrogen produced as of oxygen, there was at least a certain reasonableness in supposing that each molecule of water contained two atoms of hydrogen and one of oxygen, rather than one of each, as Dalton proposed.

Even if this were so, it remained true that 1 part of hydrogen (by weight) was combined with 8 parts of oxygen. It followed, then, that one oxygen atom was eight times as heavy as two hydrogen atoms taken together, and, therefore, sixteen times as heavy as a single hydrogen atom. If the weight of hydrogen is set at 1, then, the atomic weight of oxygen must be 16, not 8.

Avogadro's Hypothesis

The findings of Nicholson and Carlisle were strengthened by the work of a French chemist, Joseph Louis Gay-Lussac (1778–1850), who reversed matters. He discovered that 2 volumes of hydrogen combined with 1 volume of oxygen to form water. He went on to find, in fact, that when gases combined to form compounds, they always did so in small whole number ratios. Gay-Lussac announced this *law of combining volumes* in 1808.

From the whole number ratios in the formation of water from hydrogen and oxygen, it again seemed reasonable to suppose that the water molecule was composed of two atoms of hydrogen and one of oxygen. It could also be argued from similar lines of evidence that the ammonia molecule did not consist of a combination of one nitrogen atom and one hydrogen atom, but of one nitrogen atom and three hydrogen atoms. From that evidence one could conclude that the atomic weight of nitrogen was not nearly 5, but was 14.

Consider hydrogen and chlorine next. These are gases which combine to form a third gas, hydrogen chloride. One volume of hydrogen combines with one volume of chlorine, and it seems reasonable to suppose that the hydrogen chloride molecule is made up of one hydrogen atom combined with one chlorine atom.

Suppose, now, that the hydrogen gas consists of single hydrogen atoms, spaced widely apart, and the chlorine gas consists of single chlorine atoms, spaced equally widely apart. These atoms pair up to form hydrogen chloride molecules, also spaced equally widely apart.

We begin, let us say, with 100 atoms of hydrogen and 100 atoms of chlorine, giving us 200 widely spaced particles all told. The atoms pair up to form 100 molecules of hydrogen chloride. The 200 widely spaced particles (atoms) become only 100 widely spaced particles (molecules). If the spacing is equal throughout, we should find that 1 volume of hydrogen plus 1 volume of chlorine (2 volumes altogether) should yield only 1 volume of hydrogen chloride. This, however, is not so.

By actual measurement, 1 volume of hydrogen combines with 1 volume of chlorine to form 2 volumes of hydrogen chloride. Since 2 volumes to start with remain 2 volumes to end with, there must be the same number of widely spaced particles before and after.

But suppose the hydrogen gas exists not as separate atoms but as *hydrogen molecules,* each made up of 2 atoms, and that chlorine consists of *chlorine molecules,* each made up of 2 atoms. In that case, the 100 atoms of hydrogen exist as 50 widely spaced particles (molecules), and the 100 atoms of chlorine also exist as 50 widely spaced particles. In the two gases, together, there are 100 widely spaced particles altogether, half of them hydrogen-hydrogen and the other half chlorine-chlorine.

If the two gases combine, they rearrange themselves to form hydrogen-chlorine, the atomic combination making up the hydrogen chloride molecule. Since there are 100 atoms of hydrogen altogether and 100 atoms of chlorine, there are 100 molecules of hydrogen chloride (each containing one of each kind of atom).

Now we find that 50 molecules of hydrogen plus 50 molecules of chlorine combine to form 100 molecules of hydrogen chloride. This matches the actually observed 1 volume of hydrogen plus 1 volume of chlorine yielding 2 volumes of hydrogen chloride.

All this takes for granted the fact that the particles of different gases, whether composed of single atoms or of combinations of atoms, are indeed equally spaced apart, as I have been saying. If so, then equal numbers of particles of a gas (at a given temperature) would take up equal volumes no matter what the gas is.

The first to point out the necessity of this assumption that, in gases, equal numbers of particles take up equal volumes, was the Italian chemist Amedeo Avogadro (1776–1856). The assumption, advanced in 1811, is therefore known as *Avogadro's hypothesis.*

If the hypothesis is kept firmly in mind, it is possible to distinguish clearly between hydrogen atoms and hydrogen molecules (a pair of atoms) and between the atoms and molecules of other gases, too. For half a century after Avogadro's time, however, his hypothesis lay neglected, and the distinction between atoms and molecules of the important gaseous elements was not clearly defined in the minds of most chemists. Considerable uncertainty as to the value of the atomic weights of some of the most important elements persisted.

Fortunately, there were other keys to correctness in atomic weights. In 1818, for instance, a French chemist, Pierre Louis Dulong (1785–1838), and a French physicist, Alexis Thérèse Petit (1791–1820), working in collaboration, found one of them. They discovered that the specific heat of elements (the temperature rise that follows upon the absorption of a fixed quantity of heat) seemed to vary inversely with the atomic weight. That is, if element x had twice the atomic weight of element y, the temperature of element x would rise by only half as many degrees as that of element *y*, after both had absorbed the same quantity of heat. This is the *law of atomic heat*.

An element with an unknown atomic weight need then only have its specific heat measured, and at once one obtains an at least rough idea as to what its atomic weight is. This method worked only for solid elements, and not for every one of them, but it was better than nothing.

Again, a German chemist, Eilhardt Mitscherlich (1794–1863), had discovered, by 1819, that compounds known to have similar compositions tend to crystallize together, as though molecules of one intermingled with the similarly shaped molecules of the other.

It followed from this *law of isomorphism* ("same shape") that if two compounds crystallized together and if the structure of only one of them was known, the structure of the second could be assumed to be similar. This property of isomorphic crystals enabled experimenters to correct mistakes that might arise from a consideration of combining weights alone, and served as a guide to the correct atomic weights.

Weights and Symbols

The turning point came with the Swedish chemist Jöns Jakob Berzelius. He, next to Dalton himself, was chiefly responsible for the establishment of the atomic theory. About 1807, Berzelius threw himself into the determination of the exact elementary constitution of various compounds. By running many hundreds of analyses, he advanced so many examples of the law of definite proportions that the world of chemistry could no longer doubt its validity and had to accept, more or less willingly, the atomic theory which had grown directly out of the law of definite proportions.

Berzelius then set about determining atomic weights with more sophistication than Dalton had been able to do. In this project, Berzelius made use of the findings of Dulong and Petit and of Mitscherlich, as well as of Gay-Lussac's law of combining volumes. (He did not, however, use Avogadro's hypothesis.) Berzelius's first table of atomic weights, published in 1828, compares favorably, for all but two or three elements, with the accepted values of today.

An important difference between Berzelius's table and Dalton's was that Berzelius's values were not, generally, whole numbers.

Dalton's values, based on setting the atomic weight of hydrogen equal to 1, were all given as integers. This had led the English chemist William Prout (1785–1850) to suggest, in 1815, that all the elements were, after all, but composed of hydrogen. (His suggestion at first was made anonymously.) The various atoms had different weights because they were made up of different numbers of hydrogen atoms in conglomeration. This came to be called *Prout's hypothesis.*

Berzelius's table seemed to destroy this attractive suggestion (attractive, because it reduced the growing number of elements to one fundamental substance, after the fashion of the ancient Greeks, and thereby seemed to increase the order and symmetry of the universe). Thus, on a hydrogen-equals-1 basis, the atomic weight of oxygen is roughly 15.9, and oxygen can scarcely be viewed as being made up of fifteen hydrogen atoms plus nine-tenths of a hydrogen atom.

For the next century, better and better tables of atomic weights were published, and Berzelius's finding that the atomic weights of the various elements were not integral multiples of the atomic weight of hydrogen became clearer and clearer.

In the 1860s, for instance, the Belgian chemist Jean Servais Stas (1813–91) determined atomic weights more accurately than Berzelius had done. Then, at the beginning of the twentieth century, the American chemist Theodore William Richards (1868–1928), taking fantastic precautions, produced atomic weight values that may represent the ultimate accuracy possible to purely chemical methods.

If Berzelius's work had left any questions, that of Stas and Richards did not. The non-integral values of the atomic weights simply had to be accepted, and Prout's hypothesis seemed deader with each stroke. Yet even as Richards was producing his remarkably precise results, the whole problem was thrown open once again. The whole meaning of atomic weight had to be re-evaluated, and Prout's hypothesis rose from its ashes, as we shall see later.

The fact that atomic weights of the different elements were not simply related also brought up the question of the proper standard against which to measure the weight. Setting the atomic weight of hydrogen equal to 1 certainly seemed natural, and both Dalton and Berzelius tried it. Still this standard gave oxygen the uneven and inconvenient atomic weight of 15.9. It was oxygen, after all, that was usually used in determining the proportions in which particular elements combined, since oxygen combined easily with so many different elements.

To give oxygen a convenient integral atomic weight with minimum interference to the hydrogen = 1 standard, its weight was shifted from 15.9 to 16.0000. On this oxygen = 16 standard, the atomic weight of hydrogen was equal, roughly, to 1.008.

The oxygen = 16 standard was retained till the mid-twentieth century, when a more logical one, making very slight changes in atomic weight, was accepted (see page 238).

Once the atomic theory was accepted, one could picture substances as composed of molecules containing a fixed number of atoms of various elements. It seemed very natural to try to picture such molecules by drawing the correct number of little circles, each type of atom represented by a specific type of circle.

Dalton tried this symbolism. He let a simple circle represent an oxygen atom; one with a central dot a hydrogen atom; one with a vertical line a nitrogen atom; one that was solidly black, a carbon atom, and so on. Because it becomes difficult to think up sufficiently distinct circles for each element, Dalton let some be indicated by an appropriate letter. Thus sulfur was a circle containing an "S," phosphorus one that contained a "P," and so on.

Berzelius saw that the circles were superfluous and that the initials alone would do. He suggested, therefore, that each element possess a symbol standing both for the element generally and for a single atom of that element, and that this symbol consist primarily of the initial of the Latin name of the element. (Fortunately for English-speaking people, the Latin name is almost always very like the English name.) Where two or more elements possess the same initial, a second letter from the body of the name might be added. These came to be the *chemical symbols* of the elements, and are today internationally agreed upon and accepted.

Thus, the chemical symbols of carbon, hydrogen, oxygen, nitrogen, phosphorus, and sulfur are C, H, O, N, P, and S, respectively. The chemical symbols of calcium and chlorine (with carbon pre-empting the simple capital) are Ca and Cl, respectively. Only where the Latin names differ from the English are the symbols less than obvious. Thus, the chemical symbols for gold, silver, and lead are Au ("aurum"), Ag ("argentum"), and Pb ("plumbum"), respectively.

It is easy to use these symbols to indicate the number of atoms in a molecule. If the hydrogen molecule is made up of two atoms of hydrogen, it is H_2. If the water molecule contains two atoms of hydrogen and one of oxygen, it is H_2O. (The symbol without a number represents a single atom, you see.) Again, carbon dioxide is CO_2 and sulfuric acid is H_2SO_4, while hydrogen chloride is HCl. The *chemical formulas* of these simple compounds are self-explanatory.

Chemical formulas can be combined to form a *chemical equation* and describe a reaction. If one wishes to express the fact that carbon combines with oxygen to form carbon dioxide, one can write: $C + O_2 \rightarrow CO_2$.

Such equations must account for all the atoms if Lavoisier's law of conservation of mass is to be obeyed. In the equation just cited, for instance, you begin with an atom of C (carbon) and two atoms of O (the oxygen molecule), and you end with an atom of C and two atoms of O (the carbon dioxide molecule).

Suppose, though, you wished to say that hydrogen combined with chlorine to form hydrogen chloride. If this were written simply $H_2 + Cl_2 \rightarrow HCl$, it could be pointed out that there were two atoms of hydrogen and two atoms of chlorine, to begin with, but only one of each at the conclusion. To write a *balanced chemical equation,* one must say: $H_2 + Cl_2 \rightarrow 2HCl$. In the same way, to describe the combination of hydrogen and oxygen to form water, we can write a balanced equation:

$$2H_2 + O_2 \rightarrow 2H_2O.$$

Electrolysis

Meanwhile, the electric current, which had been used to such good effect by Nicholson and Carlisle, produced even more startling effects in the isolation of certain new elements.

Since Boyle's definition of "element" a century and a half before (see page 41), substances qualifying as elements by that definition were discovered in astonishing numbers. More frustratingly, some substances were known which were not elements, yet contained undiscovered elements that chemists could not manage to study in isolation.

Thus, elements are frequently found in combination with oxygen (as *oxides*). To free the element it was necessary to remove the oxygen. If a second element with a stronger affinity for oxygen were to be introduced, perhaps the oxygen would leave the first element and become attached to the second. The method was found to work. Often carbon did the trick. Thus iron ore, which is essentially iron oxide, could be heated with coke (a relatively pure form of carbon). The carbon would combine with the oxygen to form carbon monoxide and carbon dioxide, and metallic iron would be left behind.

But now consider lime instead. From its properties lime, too, seems to be an oxide. However, no known element forms lime on combination with oxygen, and one must conclude that lime is a compound of an unknown element with oxygen. To isolate that unknown element, one might try to heat lime with coke; but if so, nothing happens. The unknown element holds oxygen so strongly that carbon atoms are powerless to snatch the oxygen atoms away. Nor could any other chemical strip lime of its oxygen.

It occurred to an English chemist, Humphry Davy (1778–1829), that what could not be pulled apart by chemicals might be forced apart by the strange power of the electric current, which could pry apart the water molecule with ease when chemicals were helpless.

Davy proceeded to construct an electric battery with over 250 metallic plates, the strongest ever built up to that time. He ran intense currents from this battery through solutions of the compounds suspected of containing unknown elements, but did so without result. He obtained only hydrogen and oxygen from the water.

Apparently, he had to eliminate water. However, when he used the solid substances themselves, he could not make a current pass through them. It occurred to him, finally, to melt the compounds and pass the current through the melt. He would then, so to speak, be using a waterless, conducting liquid.

This scheme worked. On October 6, 1807, Davy passed a current through molten potash (potassium carbonate) and liberated little globules of a metal he at once labeled *potassium.* (It was so active it pulled oxygen away from water, liberating hydrogen with enough energy to cause it to burst into flame.) A week later, Davy isolated *sodium* from soda (sodium carbonate), an element only slightly less active than potassium.

In 1808, by using a somewhat modified method suggested by Berzelius, Davy isolated several metals from their oxides: *magnesium* from magnesia, *strontium* from strontia, *barium* from baryta, and *calcium* from lime. ("Calcium" is from the Latin word for lime.)

Among other things, Davy also showed that a certain greenish gas, which Scheele (see page 57) had discovered a generation earlier and thought to be an oxide, was actually an element. Davy suggested the name *chlorine,* from the Greek word for "green." Davy also showed that hydrochloric acid, although a strong acid, contained no oxygen atom in its molecules, thus disproving Lavoisier's suggestion that oxygen was a necessary component of acids (see page 62).

Davy's work on electrolysis was extended by his assistant and protégé, Michael Faraday (1791–1867), who grew to be an even greater scientist than his teacher. Faraday, in working with electrochemistry, introduced a number of terms that are still used today. (See Figure 10.) It was he, for instance, who first termed the splitting of molecules by an electric current, *electrolysis.* At the suggestion of the English classical scholar William Whewell (1794–1866 Faraday named a compound or solution which could carry an electric current, an *electrolyte.* The metal rods or strips inserted into a melt or solution, he called *electrodes;* the electrode carrying a positive charge being an *anode,* the one carrying a negative charge being a *cathode.*

The electric current was carried through the melt or solution by entities Faraday called *ions* (from a Greek word meaning "wanderer"). Those ions that traveled to the anode he called *anions;* those that traveled to the cathode were *cations.*

In 1832, he was able to announce the existence of certain quantitative relationships in electrochemistry. His *first law of electrolysis* stated: The mass of substance liberated at an electrode during electrolysis is proportional to the quantity of electricity driven through the solution. His *second law of electrolysis* stated: The weight of metal liberated by

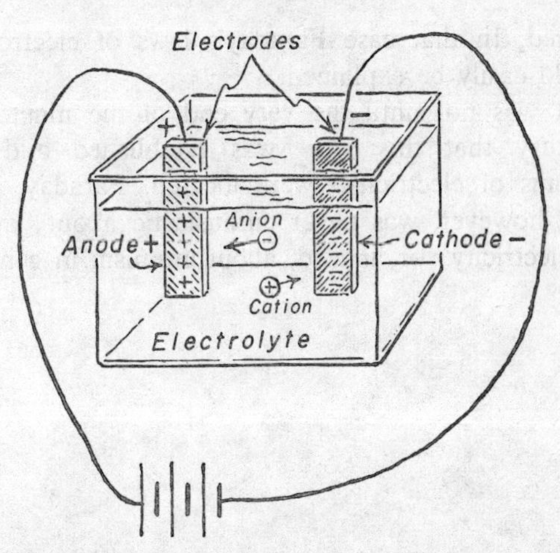

FIG. 10. Electrolytic action was explained by Faraday along the line suggested in this schematic drawing. Labels display the nomenclature he invented.

a given quantity of electricity is proportional to the equivalent weight of the metal.

Thus, if 2.7 times as much silver as potassium will combine with a given quantity of oxygen, then 2.7 times as much silver as potassium will be liberated from its compounds by a given quantity electricity.

Faraday's laws of electrolysis seemed to indicate, in the view of some chemists, that electricity could be subdivided into fixed, minimum units, as matter itself could. In other words, there were "atoms of electricity."

Suppose that when electricity passed through a solution, atoms of matter were dragged to either the cathode or the anode by "atoms of electricity." Suppose that, often, one "atom of electricity" sufficed to handle one atom of matter, but that sometimes two or even three "atoms of electricity" were required. In that case Faraday's laws of electrolysis could easily be explained.

It was not until the very end of the nineteenth century that this view was established and the "atoms of electricity" were located. Faraday, himself, however, was never enthusiastic about "atoms of electricity" or, indeed, about atomism in general.

CHAPTER 6

ORGANIC CHEMISTRY

The Breakdown of Vitalism

Ever since the discovery of fire, mankind was bound inevitably to divide substances into two classes: those that burned and those that did not. The principal fuels in early times were wood and fat or oil. Wood was a product of the plant world, while fat and oil were products of both the animal and plant world. For the most part, materials of the mineral world, such as water, sand, and the various rocks, did not burn. They tended, rather, to put out fire.

It was not hard to see, then, that the two classes of substances, combustible and non-combustible, might be considered, just as conveniently, as those which arose only from living things, and those which did not. (Of course, exceptions are to be found to this rule. Coal and sulfur, which seem products of the non-living body of the earth, are combustible.)

The accumulating knowledge of the eighteenth century showed chemists that the mere fact of combustibility was not all that divided the products of life from those of non-life. The substances characteristic of the non-living environment could withstand harsh treatment, whereas the substances originating from living or once-living matter could not. Water might be boiled and recondensed to water; iron or salt could be melted and re-frozen into the unchanged original. Olive oil or sugar, however, if heated (even under conditions that prevented burning), proceeded to fume, smoke, and char. What was left was not olive oil or sugar, nor could olive oil or sugar be formed out of it once more.

The differences seemed fundamental, and, in 1807, Berzelius suggested that substances like olive oil or sugar, the characteristic products of organisms, be called *organic.* Substances like water or salt, characteristic of the non-living environment, were *inorganic.*

A point that did not fail to impress chemists was that organic substances were easily converted, by heating or other harsh treatment, into inorganic substances. The reverse change, from inorganic to organic, was, however, unknown, at least as the nineteenth century opened.

Many chemists, at that time, considered life a special phenomenon that did not necessarily obey the laws of the universe as they applied to inanimate objects. A belief in this special position of life is called *vitalism,* and it had been strongly preached, a century earlier, by Stahl, the inventor of phlogiston (see page 46). In the light of vitalism, it seemed reasonable to suppose that some special influence (a "vital force"), operating only within living tissue, was required to convert inorganic materials into organic ones. Chemists, working with ordinary substances and techniques and without being able to manipulate a vital force in their test tubes, could not bring about this conversion.

It was for this reason, men argued, that inorganic substances might be found anywhere; in the realm of life and in that of non-life as well, as water might be found in both the ocean and the blood. Organic substances, requiring the vital force, would be found only in connection with life.

This view was first disrupted in 1828 by the work of Friedrich Wöhler (1800–82), a German chemist, who had been a pupil of Berzelius. Wöhler was particularly interested in cyanides and related compounds, and was engaged in heating a compound called ammonium cyanate. (This was widely regarded, at the time, as an inorganic substance, having no connection with living matter in any way.) In the course of the heating, Wöhler discovered he was forming crystals that resembled those of urea, a waste product eliminated in considerable quantity in the urine of many animals, including man. Closer study showed the crystals were undoubtedly urea, which was, of course, clearly an organic compound.

Wöhler repeated the experiment a number of times and found that he could convert an inorganic substance (ammonium cyanate) to an organic substance (urea) at will. He communicated this discovery to Berzelius, and that hard-headed man (who rarely condescended to be budged out of his opinions) was forced to agree that the line he had drawn between the inorganic and the organic was not as tight as he had thought.

The importance of Wöhler's feat should not be overestimated. In itself, it was not very significant. There were grounds for arguing that ammonium cyanate was not truly inorganic and, even if it were, the changeover from ammonium cyanate to urea (as was eventually made clear) was merely the result of an alteration of the positions of the atoms within the molecule. The molecule of urea was not, in any real sense, built up of a completely different substance.

Yet neither should Wöhler's feat be dismissed. If it was, in truth, a minor item in itself, it nevertheless served to break down the hold of vitalism over the minds of men.[1] It served to encourage chemists to attempt the synthesis of organic substances where otherwise they might have turned their efforts in other directions.

In 1845, for instance, Adolph Wilhelm Hermann Kolbe (1818–84), a pupil of Wöhler's, succeeded in synthesizing acetic acid, an indubitably organic substance. Furthermore, he synthesized it by a method which showed that a clear line of chemical change could be drawn from the constituent elements, carbon, hydrogen, and oxygen, to the final product, acetic acid. This *synthesis from the elements* or *total synthesis* is all that can be asked of the chemist. If Wöhler's synthesis of urea did not settle the matter of the vital force, Kolbe's synthesis of acetic acid did.

Carrying matters further was the French chemist Pierre Eugène Marcelin Berthelot (1827–1907). During the 1850s, he went about the synthesis of organic compounds systematically, turning them out in scores. These included such well-known and important substances as methyl alcohol, ethyl alcohol, methane, benzene, and acetylene. With Berthelot, crossing the line from inorganic to organic ceased to be a thrilling intrusion upon the "forbidden," and became purely routine.

The Building Blocks of Life

But the organic compounds formed by Wöhler, Kolbe, and Berthelot were all relatively simple.

[1] Actually, this was only an initial defeat for vitalism, which maintained its hold in other areas of chemistry. Despite a slow weakening of its position throughout the nineteenth century, vitalism is not entirely dead even now. For a fuller description of the various stages in the fall of vitalism, see my book, *A Short History of Biology* (Doubleday, 1964).

More characteristic of life were the far more complex substances such as starch, fats, and proteins. These were less easy to manipulate; their exact elementary makeup was less easy to determine; and on the whole they presented the budding realm of organic chemistry with a truly formidable problem.

All that could be said about them at first was that these complex substances could be broken down to relatively simple "building blocks" by heating them with dilute acid or dilute base. A Russian chemist, Gottlieb Sigismund Kirchhoff (1764–1833), was the pioneer in this respect. In 1812, he succeeded in converting starch (by heating it with acid) to a single sugar which was eventually named *glucose.*

In 1820, the French chemist Henri Braconnot treated the protein gelatin in the same fashion, and obtained the simple compound *glycine.* This was a nitrogen-containing organic acid belonging to a group of substances eventually named (by Berzelius) *amino acids.* Glycine itself proved merely the forerunner of some twenty different amino acids, all which were isolated from naturally occurring proteins over the next century.

Both starch and protein possess giant molecules that are made up (it eventually was learned) of long strings of glucose units and of amino acid units, respectively. The chemists of the nineteenth century could do little in the way of putting such long strings together in the laboratory. The case was otherwise with fats.

The French chemist Michel Eugène Chevreul (1786–1889) spent the first part of an incredibly long professional life in an investigation of fats. In 1809, he treated soap (manufactured by heating fat with alkali) with acid, and isolated what are now called *fatty acids.* Later, he showed that when fats are converted to soap, *glycerol* is removed from the fat.

Glycerol possesses a comparatively simple molecule upon which there are three logical points of attachment for additional atom groups. By the 1840s, therefore, it seemed quite logical to suppose that while starch and proteins might be made up of very many simple units, the case was otherwise with fats. Fats might be made up of just four units, one glycerol plus three fatty acids.

Berthelot stepped in here. In 1854, he heated glycerol with stearic acid, one of the more common fatty acids obtained from fats. He found that he did produce a molecule made up of a glycerol unit united to three stearic acid units. This was *tristearin,* and proved to be identical with tristearin obtained from natural fats. This was the most complicated natural product to be synthesized up to that time.

Berthelot went on to take an even more dramatic step. In place of stearic acid, he took acids that were similar but which were not obtained from natural fats themselves. These acids he heated with glycerol and obtained substances very much like ordinary fats, but not quite like any of the fats known to occur in nature.

This synthesis showed that the chemist could do more than merely duplicate the products of living tissue.[2] He could go beyond and prepare compounds that were like organic compounds in all their properties, but that were not like any organic compound actually produced by living tissue. The second half of the nineteenth century was to carry this

[2] The chemist has not actually duplicated the more complex products of living tissue even today. However, it is generally accepted that the duplication of even the most complex molecule is possible in principle; it is only time and effort that need be applied—in some cases, to be sure, a prohibitive amount of time and effort.

aspect of organic chemistry to dramatic heights indeed (see Chapter 10).

It is no wonder that by the mid-nineteenth century the division of compounds into organic and inorganic on the basis of the activity of living tissue had become obsolete. Organic compounds existed that had never been manufactured by an organism. Nevertheless, the division was still useful, for there remained important distinctions between the two classes. The distinctions were so important that the chemical techniques of the organic chemist seemed completely different from those of the inorganic chemist.

More and more it came to seem that the difference lay in chemical structure, for there two completely different kinds of molecules seemed to be involved. Most of the inorganic substances dealt with by the nineteenth-century chemist possessed small molecules made up of two to eight atoms. There were very few inorganic molecules of consequence with as many as a dozen atoms.

Even the simpler organic substances had molecules made up of a dozen atoms or more; often several dozen. As for substances such as starch and protein, they possessed, literally, giant molecules which could count their atoms by the thousands and even hundreds of thousands.

It is no wonder, then, that the complex organic molecule could easily and irreversibly be broken down even by mild disrupting influences such as gentle heat, while the simple inorganic molecules held firm under even harsh conditions.

Then, too, it became increasingly worthy of note that all organic substances, without exception, contained one or more atoms of carbon in their molecules. Almost all contained hydrogen atoms as well. Since carbon and hydrogen are themselves inflammable, it is not unexpected that compounds of which they form so important a part are also inflammable.

The German chemist Friedrich August Kekulé von Stradonitz (1829–86), usually referred to simply as Kekulé, took the logical step. In a textbook published in 1861, he defined organic chemistry as merely the chemistry of carbon compounds. Inorganic chemistry was then the chemistry of compounds that did not contain carbon. This definition has been generally accepted. It remains true, however, that a few carbon compounds, among them carbon dioxide and calcium carbonate, resemble the typical inorganic compound more than they do the typical organic compound. Such carbon compounds are usually treated at length in books on inorganic chemistry.

Isomers and Radicals

The simple inorganic compounds involved in the great chemical advances of the eighteenth century had easily been interpreted in atomic terms. It seemed quite sufficient to indicate the different types of atoms present in each molecule and the number of each. One could write the oxygen molecule as O_2, hydrogen chloride as HCl, ammonia as NH_3, sodium sulfate as Na_2SO_4, and so on.

Such formulas, giving nothing more than the number of each type of atom present in the molecule, are called *empirical formulas*. (The word "empirical" means "determined by experiment.") It was natural to feel, in the first decades of the nineteenth century, that each different compound had a distinct empirical formula of its own and that no two compounds could have the same empirical formula.

Organic substances, with their large molecules,

were troublesome from the start. The empirical formula of morphine (quite a simple organic compound as compared with proteins, for instance) is now known to be $C_{17}H_{19}NO_3$. It would have been most difficult, using early nineteenth-century techniques, perhaps even impossible, to decide whether that or, say, $C_{16}H_{20}NO_3$, were correct. The empirical formula of acetic acid, much simpler (it is $C_2H_4O_2$) than that of morphine, aroused considerable controversy in the first half of the nineteenth century. Nevertheless, if chemists were to learn anything about the molecular structure of organic substances, they had to start with empirical formulas.

In the 1780s, Lavoisier had tried to determine the relative proportions of carbon and hydrogen in organic compounds by burning them and weighing the carbon dioxide and water produced. His results had not been very accurate. In the first years of the nineteenth century, Gay-Lussac (discoverer of the law of combining volumes, see page 80) and his colleague, the French chemist Louis Jacques Thénard (1777–1857), introduced an improvement. They mixed the organic substance with an *oxidizing agent,* such as potassium chlorate. On heating, this combination yielded oxygen, and the oxygen, intimately mixed with the organic substance, brought about its more rapid and complete combustion. By collecting the carbon dioxide and water formed on combustion, Gay-Lussac and Thénard could determine the relative proportion of carbon and hydrogen in the original compound. With Dalton's theory now advanced, this proportion could be expressed in atomic terms.

Many organic compounds were made up only of carbon, hydrogen, and oxygen. With carbon and hydrogen determined and oxygen assumed to account for whatever was left over, an empirical formula could often be worked out. By 1811, Gay-Lussac had worked out the empirical formulas for some of the simple sugars, for instance.

This procedure was improved further by a German chemist, Justus von Liebig (1803–73) who, by 1831, could obtain fairly reliable empirical formulas as a result.[3] Soon afterward, in 1833, the French chemist Jean Baptiste André Dumas (1800–84) devised a modification of the method, one which allowed the chemist to collect nitrogen also among the products of combustion. In this way one could determine the proportions of nitrogen in an organic substance.

These pioneers in *organic analysis,* in the course of their researches, produced results that shattered the belief in the importance of the empirical formula. It came about this way:

In 1824, Liebig studied a group of compounds, the *fulminates,* while Wöhler (who was to become a fast friend of Liebig, and who was soon to synthesize urea, see page 95) was studying another group of compounds, the *cyanates.* Both sent reports concerning their work to a journal edited by Gay-Lussac.

Gay-Lussac noted that the empirical formulas given for these compounds were identical, and yet the properties described were quite different. (As an example, both silver cyanate and silver fulminate consist of molecules containing one atom each of silver, carbon, nitrogen, and oxygen.)

[3] Liebig was one of the great chemistry teachers of all time. He taught at the University of Giessen, where he established the first real laboratory course in chemistry. Numerous chemists studied with him and learned laboratory procedures from him. Liebig was one of the influences making chemistry, in which France had been pre-eminent in the eighteenth century, almost a German monopoly in the nineteenth century.

Gay-Lussac reported this observation to Berzelius, then the most noted chemist in the world, but Berzelius was reluctant to believe the discovery. By 1830, however, Berzelius himself had discovered that two organic compounds, *racemic acid* and *tartaric acid,* although possessing different properties, seemed to have the same empirical formula (now known to be $C_4H_6O_6$).

Since elements were present in these different compounds in the same proportions, Berzelius suggested that such compounds be termed *isomers* (from Greek words meaning "equal proportions"), and the suggestion was adopted. In succeeding decades, more and more cases of isomerism were discovered.

It seemed clear that if two molecules were made up of the same number of the same kinds of atoms and yet were different in properties, the difference must lie in the manner in which the atoms were arranged within the molecule. In the case of the simple molecules of the better-known inorganic compounds, it might be that only one arrangement of the atoms within the molecule was possible. For that reason, no isomers would arise and the empirical formula would be sufficient. Thus, H_2O would be water and nothing else.

In the more complicated organic molecules, however, there would be room for different arrangements and, therefore, for isomers. In the case of the cyanates and fulminates, the different arrangements are easy to discover, for each molecule contains but a few atoms. Silver cyanate can be written AgOCN, while silver fulminate is AgNCO.

Here only four atoms are involved. With still more atoms, the number of possible arrangements becomes so great that it is difficult indeed to decide just which arrangements fit which compounds. Even the case of racemic acid and tartaric acid, with sixteen atoms to the molecule, was too difficult to handle in the first half of the nineteenth century. The situation would grow simply impossible (so it might have seemed) if still larger molecules were considered.

The problem of molecular structure might have had to be abandoned as hopeless almost as soon as the very existence of the problem had been recognized, had not a possibility of simplification appeared.

In 1810 and thereafter, Gay-Lussac and Thénard were working with hydrogen cyanide (HCN), which they showed to be an acid, although it didn't contain oxygen. (This, like Davy's nearly simultaneous discovery of the same fact concerning hydrochloric acid–see page 90–disproved Lavoisier's belief that oxygen was the characteristic element of acids.) Gay-Lussac and Thénard found that the CN combination (the *cyanide group*) could be shifted from compound to compound, without its breaking apart into individual carbon and nitrogen atoms. The CN combination, in fact, acted much as a single atom of chlorine or bromine might act, so that sodium cyanide (NaCN) had some properties in common with sodium chloride (NaCl) and sodium bromide (NaBr).[4]

Such a group of two (or more) atoms that remain in combination while being shifted from one molecule to another was termed a *radical,* from the Latin word for "root." The reason for the name was that molecules, it was believed, might be built up of a limited number of small atom combinations.

[4] "Some properties" does not, most emphatically, mean all properties. Sodium chloride is essential to life, sodium bromide has mild toxic effects, and sodium cyanide is a virulent, fast-acting poison.

The radicals would then be the "roots" out of which the molecule would, so to speak, grow.

Of course, the CN group was a very simple one, but a considerably more complex case was demonstrated by Wöhler and Liebig, working together. They discovered that the *benzoyl group* could be switched from one molecule to another without being disrupted. The empirical formula of the benzoyl group is now known to be C_7H_5O.

In short, it began to appear that to solve the structural mystery of large molecules, one must first solve the structures of a certain number of different radicals. The molecules could then be constructed, without much difficulty (it was hoped), out of the radicals. Things were looking up!

CHAPTER 7

MOLECULAR STRUCTURE

The Theory of Types

Berzelius seized upon the notion that radicals could be the units of which organic molecules were built. He believed that organic molecules were built of radicals as inorganic molecules were built of individual atoms. Radicals, he came to think, were almost as indivisible and untouchable as the individual atoms themselves.

Berzelius maintained that the force holding atoms together in an inorganic molecule or in an organic radical was electrical in nature (which eventually turned out to be right, as a matter of fact). Every molecule, then, had to contain a positive portion and a negative portion, since only between oppositely charged elements was there attraction.

For simple inorganic substances, like sodium chloride, this notion of positive and negative was eventually shown to fit the facts well (see page 206). To make it fit organic substances, Berzelius had to insist that radicals consisted of carbon and hydrogen only, with carbon negative and hydrogen positive. He held, therefore, that the benzoyl radical (C_7H_5O) did not and could not contain oxygen, which distorted the work done with that radical. Berzelius was also certain that it was impossible to substitute a negative element for a positive element without drastically changing the properties of a compound.

He was quickly shown to be wrong in that last contention. Dumas (see page 102) was an enthusiastic supporter of Berzelius, but one of Dumas's pupils, Auguste Laurent (1807–53) managed, in 1836, to substitute chlorine atoms for several of the hydrogen atoms in the molecule of ethyl alcohol. This experiment delivered the fatal blow to Berzelius's views, for chlorine was considered negative and hydrogen positive, yet one could be substituted for the other without making a drastic change in the properties of a compound.

Furthermore, in this chlorinated compound, carbon must be attached directly to chlorine, and if both consisted of negative atoms, how could that be? Negative electric charges repelled each other. (For that matter, how could two chlorine atoms hold together to form a chlorine molecule? Such matters were not settled for another century, as we shall see on page 222.)

Berzelius, grown testy and extremely conservative in his old age, refused to change his notions. Upon hearing of Laurent's report, he attacked the new findings ferociously. Dumas had himself, in 1839, substituted chlorine for three of the hydrogen atoms in acetic acid. Nevertheless, in the face of Berzelius's displeasure, Dumas rather cravenly backed down and disowned Laurent.

Laurent held firm, however, and continued to accumulate evidence to the effect that radicals were not as indestructible and untouchable as Berzelius insisted, and that one must not overemphasize the matter of positive and negative. Berzelius's anger barred Laurent from the more famous laboratories, and while Berzelius lived, his version of the radical theory remained in being by the sheer force of his personality. With Berzelius's death in 1848, however, his theory died and Laurent's gained popularity.

Laurent abandoned all emphasis on electrical forces. He believed that an organic molecule had a nucleus (which might be a single atom) to which different radicals might be attached. Organic molecules might then be grouped into families or *types* (hence, the *theory of types*). All the members of one type would have an identical nucleus to which any of a series of similar radicals could be attached; and within the radicals there would be considerable room for variation.

A particular molecular type might even extend into the realm of the inorganic.

For instance, the water molecule (H_2O) may be viewed as consisting of a central oxygen atom (the nucleus) to which two hydrogen atoms are attached. If, in place of one hydrogen atom, any of a series of radicals is substituted, a type of compound is built up that includes among its members water as well as various organic molecules.

If one substituted for the hydrogen atom a methyl group (CH_3) or an ethyl group (C_2H_5), one would have CH_3OH (*methyl alcohol*), and C_2H_5OH (*ethyl alcohol*), respectively. A vast number of other *alcohols* could be built up in the same way. And, indeed, alcohols not only have many similarities among themselves, but, as a class, also show certain resemblances to water. The simpler alcohols, such as methyl alcohol and ethyl alcohol, will mix with water in all proportions. Sodium metal will react with alcohols as it will with water, though more slowly, and so on.

Between 1850 and 1852, the English chemist Alexander William Williamson (1824–1904) showed that the family of organic compounds called *ethers* could also be built up about the "water type." In their case both the hydrogens of water were substituted by organic radicals. The common ether, then beginning to be used as an anesthetic, has both hydrogens replaced by ethyl groups, so that it is $C_2H_5OC_2H_5$.

Earlier, in 1848, the French chemist Charles Adolphe Wurtz (1817–84) had studied a group of compounds related to ammonia and called, therefore, *amines*. He showed they belonged to a type with a nitrogen nucleus. In ammonia a nitrogen atom was bound to three hydrogens. In amines organic radicals replaced one or more of these hydrogens.

The theory of types gained in popularity because it could be used to organize the rapidly proliferating numbers of organic compounds being studied. The Russo-German chemist Friedrich Konrad Beilstein (1838–1906) published a vast compendium of organic compounds in 1880, and utilized Laurent's theory of type to organize those compounds into a rational order.

Nevertheless, the theory, as it emerged from Laurent's work, remained incomplete. It still made use of radicals as units, and the question of molecular structure was evaded rather than answered. For a proper answer, one had to face up to the question: What is the actual atomic arrangement within the radicals themselves?

Valence

The theory of types impressed some chemists with the point that the oxygen atom consistently combined with two other atoms or radicals. It might combine with two hydrogen atoms to form water, with one hydrogen atom and an organic radical to form an alcohol, or with two organic radicals to form an ether. But always the oxygen atom attached itself to two entities.

In similar fashion, the nitrogen atom would always combine with three atoms or radicals. Men like Kolbe (see page 96) took to writing formulas for organic compounds in which such a constancy in the number of attachments to oxygen or nitrogen was taken for granted.

The point was made general by an English chemist, Edward Frankland (1825–99). He was the first to become interested in *organo-metallic compounds,* those in which organic groupings were attached to atoms of metals such as zinc.[1] Here it was quite clear that each metallic atom would attach to itself only so many organic groupings, and that this number was different for different metals. Zinc atoms, for instance, would combine with two organic groupings, neither more nor less.

In 1852, Frankland advanced what later came to be known as the theory of *valence* (from a Latin word for "power"), which is the statement that each atom has a fixed combining power. For instance, a hydrogen atom, under ordinary conditions, will combine with only one other atom. This is also true of sodium, chlorine, silver, bromine, and potassium. All have a valence of 1.

Oxygen atoms may combine with as many as two different atoms, as will calcium, sulfur, magnesium, and barium. All these elements have a valence of

[1] In the true organo-metallic compound, the atom of the metal is firmly attached to a carbon atom. Compounds such as zinc acetate (a type of substance known prior to Frankland's time) are salts of organic acids. In such salts the atom of the metal is attached to an oxygen atom, and these are not considered true organo-metallic compounds.

2. Nitrogen, phosphorus, aluminum, and gold have a valence of 3. Iron could have a valence of either 2 or 3, and so on. The matter of valence turned out, in the long run, to be nothing like as simple as it seemed at first. Nevertheless, even the simple form of the theory proved to be of inestimable worth.

For one thing, the concept of valence helped to clarify the difference between atomic weight (see page 77) and equivalent weight (see page 91) of an element. Even as late as the mid-nineteenth century, many chemists confused the two.

It can be determined that 1 part of hydrogen will combine with 35.5 parts of chlorine, since 1 atom of hydrogen will combine with 1 atom of chlorine to form hydrogen chloride, and the chlorine atom is 35.5 times as heavy as the hydrogen atom. That is, chlorine has an atomic weight of 35.5. But 1 part of hydrogen will not combine with all elements in proportion to their atomic weights. For instance, oxygen has an atomic weight of 16, but each oxygen atom combines with two hydrogen atoms, since oxygen has a valence of 2. Therefore, 16 parts of oxygen combine with 2 parts of hydrogen. The equivalent weight of oxygen is the quantity of oxygen that combines with 1 part of hydrogen, and that is 16/2 or 8.

In the same way, the nitrogen atom, with an atomic weight of 14 and a valence of 3, combines with 3 hydrogen atoms. The equivalent weight of nitrogen is therefore 14/3 or about 4.7.

In general, the equivalent weight of an atom is equal to its atomic weight divided by its valence.

Again, Faraday's second law of electrolysis (see page 90) states that the weight of different metals liberated by a given quantity of electric current is proportional to the equivalent weights of those metals. This means that a given amount of electric current will liberate only half as much by weight of a 2-valent metal as it would of a 1-valent metal of about equal atomic weight.

This situation can be explained by supposing that one "atom of electricity" (see page 91) is required to transport a single 1-valent atom, while two are required for a single 2-valent atom. This connection of valence and "atoms of electricity" was not fully appreciated, however, for another half-century (see page 222).

Structural Formulas

The notion of valence was applied with particular force to the structure of organic molecules by Kekulé (mentioned earlier on page 100). He began with the suggestion that carbon had a valence of 4 and proceeded, in 1858, to work out the structure of the simpler organic molecules and radicals on that basis. The concept could be visualized after a Scottish chemist, Archibald Scott Couper (1831–92), suggested that these combining forces between atoms (*bonds,* as they are usually called) be pictured in the form of small dashes. In this way, organic molecules could be built up like so many "Tinker-toy" structures.

Indeed, this representation made it possible to visualize quite clearly why organic molecules were so much larger and more complex, on the whole, than inorganic molecules. According to the Kekulé concept, carbon atoms could attach themselves to each other by means of one or more of their four valence bonds to form long chains, either straight or branched. No other kind of atom seemed to have that ability in nearly as marked a fashion as carbon did.

Thus, the three simplest *hydrocarbons* (molecules made up of carbon and hydrogen atoms only), which are methane (CH_4), ethane (C_2H_6), and propane (C_3H_8), could be pictured with every carbon atom possessing four bonds and every hydrogen atom possessing one, as follows:

```
    H              H   H            H   H   H
    |              |   |            |   |   |
H — C — H      H — C — C — H    H — C — C — C — H
    |              |   |            |   |   |
    H              H   H            H   H   H
 methane          ethane             propane
```

This series could be continued by stringing together carbon atoms for almost as long as one would care to. By adding oxygen with two bonds and nitrogen with three, one could represent the molecule of ethyl alcohol (C_2H_6O), and methylamine (CH_5N) as follows:

```
    H   H                  H
    |   |                  |
H — C — C — O — H      H — C — N — H
    |   |                  |   |
    H   H                  H   H
  ethyl alcohol         methylamine
```

Such *structural formulas* could be made more flexible if the existence of two bonds (a *double bond*) or three (a *triple bond*) between adjacent atoms were permitted. Thus, ethylene (C_2H_4), acetylene (C_2H_2), methyl cyanide (C_2H_3N), acetone (C_3H_6O), and acetic acid ($C_2H_4O_2$) could be represented as follows:

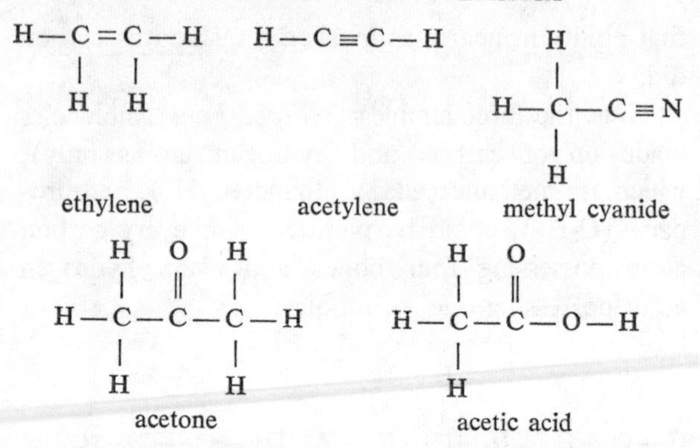

Structural formulas showed such obvious usefulness that a number of organic chemists accepted them at once. They completely outmoded all attempts to depict organic molecules as structures built up of radicals. Nothing less than an atom-by-atom picture would do now.

In particular, a Russian chemist, Alexander Mikhailovich Butlerov (1828–86), supported the new system. During the 1860s, he pointed out how the use of structural formulas could explain the existence of isomers (see page 103). For instance, to use a very simple case, ethyl alcohol and dimethyl ether, although possessing widely different properties, have the same empirical formula: C_2H_6O. The structural formulas of the two compounds are:

```
    H   H              H       H
    |   |              |       |
H — C — C — O — H  H — C — O — C — H
    |   |              |       |
    H   H              H       H
 ethyl alcohol       dimethyl ether
```

It is no wonder that the change in arrangement of atoms leads to two sets of widely different properties. In the case of ethyl alcohol, one of the six hydrogen atoms is attached to an oxygen atom, while in dimethyl ether all six are attached to carbon atoms. The oxygen atom holds the hydrogen atom more weakly than the carbon atom does, so that sodium metal added to ethyl alcohol replaces just one-sixth of the hydrogen content. If sodium is added to dimethyl ether, it displaces no hydrogen at all. Thus, chemical reactions serve as guides to structural formulas, and the formulas in turn serve as guides to understanding reactions.

Butlerov dealt specifically with a type of isomerism called *tautomerism,* in which certain substances always appeared as mixtures of two compounds. If one of these compounds were isolated in pure form, it would promptly change over, in part, to the other. Butlerov showed that tautomerism consisted of a spontaneous shift of a hydrogen atom from a connection with an oxygen atom to a connection with a nearby carbon atom (and back again).

A major problem in the first few years of the structural formula involved *benzene,* a simple hydrocarbon with the empirical formula C_6H_6. No structural formula seemed to satisfy the valence requirements and at the same time to account for the great stability of the compound. That is, the structural formulas that were first suggested resembled those of other compounds which were very unstable.

Again it was Kekulé to the rescue. One day in 1865 (according to Kekulé himself), while in a semi-doze on a bus, it seemed to him that he saw atoms whirling in a dance. Suddenly, the tail-end of one chain attached itself to the head-end and formed a spinning ring. Until then structural formulas had been built up only of *chains* of carbon atoms, but now Kekulé fastened on the notion of rings of carbon atoms as well. He suggested the following structural formula for benzene:

```
           H
           |
  H        C        H
   \     //  \     /
      C          C
      |          ||
      C          C
   /     \\  /     \
  H        C        H
           |
           H
```

benzene

This explanation was accepted, and the concept of the structural formula was placed on a firmer basis than ever.[2]

Optical Isomers

Despite the usefulness of the structural formulas of Kekulé, they did not entirely account for one particularly subtle type of isomerism. This involved light, which we must therefore briefly consider.

In 1801, Thomas Young (1773–1829), an extraordinary Englishman who was the first to understand the physiology of the eye, had conducted experiments which demonstrated that light behaved as though it consisted of tiny waves. Then, about 1814, Augustin Jean Fresnel, a French physicist (1788–1827), showed that the light waves belonged to the particular class known as *transverse waves.* These waves oscillate at right angles to the direction in which the wave as a whole is traveling. This situa-

[2] Nevertheless, the presence of three double bonds in benzene created a problem, for compounds with double bonds usually underwent certain types of reactions which benzene did not ordinarily undergo. It was nearly three-quarters of a century before the puzzle of the double bonds that didn't act like double bonds was explained (see page 184).

tion is best visualized in connection with water waves, which are transverse in nature. Individual bits of water move up and down, but the wave itself moves outward.

Light waves are not confined to a surface and so need not merely move up and down. They can move right and left, or northeast and southwest, or northwest and southeast. In fact, there is an infinite number of directions in which a light wave can oscillate at right angles to its direction of travel. In a beam of ordinary light some waves are oscillating in one direction, some in another, some in still another. There is no one direction that is preferred.

If such a beam of light is sent through certain crystals, however, the orderly arrangement of atoms within the crystals forces the light beam to oscillate in some particular plane–a plane that will allow the light to slip past and between the rows of atoms.

Light oscillating in one plane only is called *polarized light*. This name was given it in 1808 by a French physicist, Etienne Louis Malus (1775–1812). At that time, the wave theory had not yet been accepted, and Malus had a notion that light consisted of particles with north and south poles, and that in polarized light, all the poles were lined in the same direction. This theory quickly vanished, but the expression remained and is still used.

The properties and behavior of polarized light seemed to lie exclusively in the province of the physicist until 1815. In that year a French physicist, Jean Baptiste Biot (1774–1862), showed that if polarized light passed through certain crystals, the plane in which the waves undulated was rotated. Sometimes it was rotated in clockwise fashion (*dextrorotation*), sometimes in counterclockwise fashion (*levorotation*).

Among the crystals displaying this property of

optical activity were those of organic compounds. Furthermore, some of these organic compounds, such as the various sugars, showed optical activity even when not in crystalline form, but in solution instead.

As it eventually turned out, there were substances that differed only in their optical properties. Otherwise identical, one substance would rotate the plane of polarized light clockwise, the other would rotate it counterclockwise. Sometimes still a third would not rotate the plane at all. The isomers racemic acid and tartaric acid, which Berzelius had discovered (see page 103), differed in optical properties.

Such *optical isomers* were not readily explained by Kekulé's structural formulas.

The first glimmer of understanding of optical activity appeared in 1848, when the French chemist Louis Pasteur (1822–95) began work with crystals of sodium ammonium tartrate.

Pasteur noted that the crystals were asymmetric; that is, one side of a crystal had a small facet not present on the other. In some crystals the facet was present on the right side, in others on the left. Using a magnifying glass, he painstakingly separated the crystals with tweezers and dissolved each group separately. The properties of the solutions seemed identical but for the optical activity. One solution was dextrorotatory, the other levorotatory.

It seemed, then, that optical activity was the result of asymmetry. It seemed also that whether the plane of polarized light was twisted in one direction or another depended on whether otherwise identical crystals had a "right-handed" asymmetry or a "left-handed" one.

This theory was satisfactory when applied to crystals, but what about optical activity that persisted in solution? In solution substances existed not as crystals but as individual molecules floating about randomly. If optical activity had to imply asymmetry, then the asymmetry had to exist in the molecular structure itself.

The Kekulé structural formulas did not show the necessary asymmetry, but this lack did not necessarily disprove the connection between asymmetry and optical activity. After all, the Kekulé structural formulas were written two-dimensionally on the flat surface of a blackboard or a piece of paper. Surely, it was not to be expected that in reality organic molecules were two-dimensional.

It seemed certain that the atoms in a molecule must be distributed three-dimensionally. If they were, their arrangement then might well show the necessary asymmetry to account for optical activity. However, how was one to go about applying the necessary three-dimensionality to the molecule?

Atoms had never been seen and their very existence might simply be a convenient fiction used to explain chemical reactions. Was it safe to take their existence so literally that one should distribute them in three dimensions?

A young man was needed to take the next step, one who had not yet gained the wise caution that comes with years.

Molecules in Three Dimensions

Such a person was the young Dutch chemist Jacobus Hendricus Van't Hoff (1852–1911). In 1874 he had not yet completed work for his Ph.D., but he daringly suggested that the four bonds of the carbon atom were distributed in three-dimensional space toward the four apices of a tetrahedron.

To see this, imagine that three of the bonds of the carbon atom are arranged so as to resemble the legs of a squat tripod, while the fourth bond sticks directly upward. Each bond is then equidistant from the remaining three, and the angle between one bond and any of its neighbors is about 109°. (See Figure 11.)

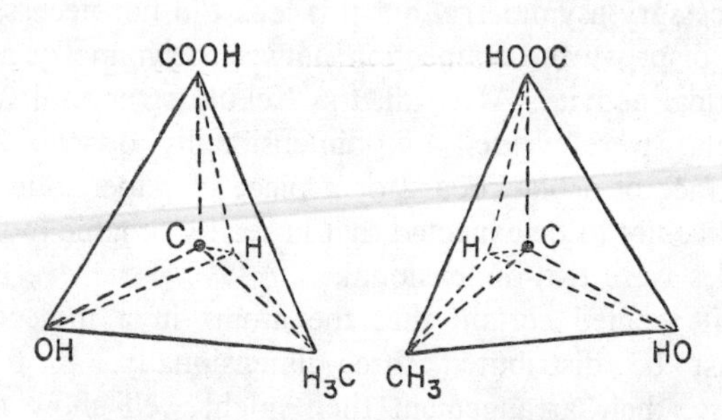

FIG. 11. Tetrahedral bonding of carbon atoms permits two configurations of atoms in compounds, one being the mirror image of the other. This model shows the mirror-image arrangements of the lactic acid molecule, $CH_3 \cdot CHOH \cdot CO_2H$.

The four bonds of the carbon atom are thus arranged symmetrically about the atom, and asymmetry is introduced only when each of the four bonds is attached to a different kind of atom or group of atoms. Then the four attachments can be arranged in exactly two different fashions, one being the mirror image of the other. This pattern provides exactly the type of asymmetry Pasteur had found in his crystals.

Almost simultaneously, the French chemist Joseph Achille Le Bel (1847–1930) published a similar suggestion. The tetrahedral carbon atom is sometimes referred to as the *Van't Hoff-Le Bel theory*.

The tetrahedral atom explained so much so neatly that it was quickly accepted. Aiding in this was a book published in 1887 by the German chemist

Johannes Adolf Wislicenus (1835–1902), which placed the authority of an older and particularly well-respected scientist behind the theory.

Most important of all, there was no blinking the facts. Compounds possessing *asymmetric carbon atoms* (those connected to four different types of groupings) possessed optical activity, while those that did not possess such atoms did not. Furthermore, the number of optical isomers was always equal to the number predicted by the Van't Hoff-Le Bel theory.

In the final decades of the nineteenth century the three-dimensional view of bonding was extended beyond the carbon atom.

The German chemist Viktor Meyer (1848–97) showed that the bonds of nitrogen atoms, if viewed three-dimensionally, could also explain certain types of optical isomerism. The English chemist William Jackson Pope (1870–1939) showed this was applicable to other atoms, such as those of sulfur, selenium, and tin; the German-Swiss Alfred Werner (1866–1919) added cobalt, chromium, rhodium, and other metals.

(Beginning in 1891, Werner developed a *coordination theory* of molecular structure, the idea for which, according to him, came to him in his sleep, waking him at 2 A.M. with a start. Essentially, this theory held that the structural relationships between atoms did not need to be restricted to ordinary valence bonds. Instead, particularly in certain comparatively complex inorganic molecules, atom groups could be distributed about some central atom in accordance with certain geometric principles that did not seem to take ordinary valence into account. It was nearly half a century before notions of valence became subtle enough to include both the simple compounds fitting the notions of Frankland and

Kekulé, and the *coordination compounds* of Werner as well.)

The idea of three-dimensional structure led quickly to further developments. Viktor Meyer had shown that while atom groupings ordinarily could rotate freely about a single bond attaching them to the rest of the molecule, the bulk of nearby groups of atoms sometimes prevented this rotation. This situation, called *steric hindrance,* can be likened to a door that ordinarily moves freely on its hinges but may be blocked by some obstruction behind it. Pope went on to show that through steric hindrance it was possible for a molecule to be asymmetric as a whole. It would then show optical activity even though none of the constituent atoms were asymmetric in themselves.

The German chemist Johann Friedrich Wilhelm Adolf von Baeyer (1835–1917) used the three-dimensional view, in 1885, to picture carbon atoms arranged in planar rings. If the four bonds of the carbon atoms are pointed toward the four corners of a tetrahedron, the angle between any two of them is about 109.5°. Baeyer argued that in any organic compound there was a tendency to allow the carbon atoms to be so connected that the bonds remained at their natural angles. If the angle is forced to change, the atom is placed under a strain.

If three carbon atoms were bound in a ring, they would form an equilateral triangle, with the angle between each pair of bonds equal to 60°. This separation is considerably different from the natural 109.5° angle, and for that reason 3-carbon rings are hard to form and, once formed, are easy to break up.

A 4-carbon ring would form a square, with the angles 90°; a 5-carbon ring would form a pentagon with angles 108°; a 6-carbon ring would form a hexagon with angles 120°. It would seem then that a 5-carbon ring involves virtually no strain on the bonds of the carbon atom, and a 6-carbon ring involves only a small amount of strain. Baeyer's *strain theory* seemed to account, therefore, for the preponderance of such rings in nature over rings of more than six or less than five atoms.[3]

Most dramatic of all, perhaps, was the work, in the 1880s, of the German chemist Emil Fischer (1852–1919) on the chemistry of the simple sugars. A number of well-known sugars share the identical empirical formula of $C_6H_{12}O_6$. They also have many properties in common, but differ in others, notably in the extent of their optical activity.

Fischer showed that each such sugar had four asymmetric carbon atoms, and that on the basis of the Van't Hoff-Le Bel theory, there should therefore be sixteen optical isomers. These isomers should be arranged in eight pairs; in each pair one isomer should rotate the plane of polarized light clockwise to exactly the extent the other isomer rotates it counterclockwise.

Fischer proceeded to work out the exact arrangement of the atoms in each of the sixteen isomers. The fact that exactly sixteen isomers of the 6-carbon sugars have been found, divided into eight pairs, is strong evidence for the worth of the Van't Hoff-Le Bel theory. This same accuracy in prediction holds in the case of other types of sugars, of amino acids, and of any other types of compound.

By 1900, the depiction of molecular structure in three dimensions, having well proved its value, was universally accepted.

[3] Baeyer's strain theory applies to rings with atoms in a single plane. It is not necessary for the atoms to be in a single plane, and all sorts of odd rings can be (and are) formed in which this restriction does not hold.

CHAPTER 8

THE PERIODIC TABLE

Elements in Disorder

There is a curious parallel in the histories of the organic chemistry and inorganic chemistry of the nineteenth century. The opening decades of the century saw a puzzling proliferation in the number of organic compounds, and also in the number of elements. The third quarter of the century saw the realm of organic compounds reduced to order, thanks to Kekulé's structural formula. It saw the realm of elements reduced to order also, and at least part of the credit for both changes goes to events at a particular international meeting of chemists.

But let's begin with the disorder at the beginning of the century.

The discovery of elements over and above the nine known to the ancients and the four studied by medieval alchemists has been mentioned in Chapter 4. The gaseous elements, nitrogen, hydrogen, oxygen, and chlorine, had all been discovered in the eighteenth century. So had the metals, cobalt, platinum, nickel, manganese, tungsten, molybdenum, uranium, titanium, and chromium.

In the first decade of the nineteenth century, no less than fourteen new elements were added to the list. Among the chemists already mentioned in this book, Davy had isolated no fewer than six by means of electrolysis (see page 89). Gay-Lussac and Thénard had isolated boron; Wollaston had isolated palladium and rhodium, while Berzelius had discovered cerium.

Then, too, the English chemist Smithson Tennant (1761–1815), for whom Wollaston had worked as an assistant, discovered osmium and iridium. Another English chemist, Charles Hatchett (c. 1765–1847), isolated columbium (now officially called niobium), while a Swedish chemist, Anders Gustaf Ekeberg (1767–1813), discovered tantalum.

The haul in succeeding decades was not quite as rich, but the number of elements continued to mount. Berzelius discovered four more elements, for instance: selenium, silicon, zirconium, and thorium. (See Figure 12.) Louis Nicolas Vauquelin in 1797 discovered beryllium.

By 1830, fifty-five different elements were recognized, a long step from the four elements of ancient theory. In fact, the number was too great for the comfort of chemists. The elements varied widely in properties and there seemed little order about them. Why were there so many? And how many more yet remained to be found? Ten? A hundred? A thousand? An infinite number?

It was tempting to search for order in the list of elements already known. Perhaps in this manner some reason for the number of elements might be found and some way of accounting for the variation of properties that existed.

The first to catch a glimmering of order was the German chemist Johann Wolfgang Döbereiner (1780–1849). In 1829, he noted that the element bromine, discovered three years earlier by the French chemist Antoine Jérôme Balard (1802–76), seemed just halfway in its properties between chlorine and iodine. (Iodine had been discovered by

ATOMIC WEIGHTS

Element	Atomic Weight	Element	Atomic Weight
Aluminum	26.98	Nickel	58.71
Antimony	121.76	Niobium	92.91
Arsenic	74.91	Nitrogen	14.008
Barium	137.36	Osmium	190.2
Beryllium	9.013	Oxygen	16.0000
Bismuth	209.00	Palladium	106.4
Boron	10.82	Phosphorus	30.975
Bromine	79.916	Platinum	195.09
Cadmium	112.41	Potassium	39.100
Calcium	40.08	Rhodium	102.91
Carbon	12.011	Selenium	78.96
Cerium	140.13	Silicon	28.09
Chlorine	35.457	Silver	107.88
Chromium	52.01	Sodium	22.991
Cobalt	58.94	Strontium	87.63
Copper	63.54	Sulfur	32.066
Gold	197.0	Tantalum	180.95
Hydrogen	1.0080	Tellurium	127.61
Iodine	126.91	Thorium	232.05
Iridium	192.2	Tin	118.70
Iron	55.85	Titanium	47.90
Lead	207.21	Tungsten	183.86
Lithium	6.940	Uranium	238.07
Magnesium	24.32	Vanadium	50.95
Manganese	54.94	Yttrium	88.92
Mercury	200.61	Zinc	65.38
Molybdenum	95.95	Zirconium	91.22

FIG. 12. Fifty-four elements known at the time of Berzelius's discoveries are listed here, with the atomic weights calculated on the basis of oxygen at 16.0000. (From *The Search for the Elements*, Basic Books.)

another French chemist, Bernard Courtois [1777–1838], in 1811.) Not only did chlorine, bromine, and iodine show a smooth gradation in such properties as color and reactivity, but the atomic weight of bromine seemed to lie just midway between those of chlorine and iodine. Coincidence?

Döbereiner went on to find two other groups of three elements exhibiting neat gradations of properties: calcium, strontium, and barium; and sulfur, selenium, and tellurium. In both groups the atomic weight of the element in the middle was about midway between those of the other two. Coincidence again?

Döbereiner called these groups "triads," and searched unsuccessfully for others. The fact that five-sixths of the known elements could not be fitted into any triad arrangement made chemists decide that Döbereiner's findings were merely coincidence. Furthermore, the manner in which atomic weights fit along with the chemical properties among the elements of Döbereiner's triads did not impress chemists generally. In the first half of the nineteenth century, atomic weights tended to be underestimated. They were convenient in making chemical calculations, but there seemed no reason to use them in making lists of the elements, for instance.

It was even doubtful that atomic weights were useful in making chemical calculations. Some chemists did not distinguish carefully between atomic weight and molecular weight; some did not distinguish between atomic weight and equivalent weight. Thus, the equivalent weight of oxygen is 8 (see page 76), the atomic weight is 16, and the molecular weight 32. In chemical calculations the equivalent weight, 8, is handiest; why then should the number 16 be used to determine the place of oxygen in the list of elements?

This confusion among equivalent weight, atomic weight, and molecular weight spread its disorganizing influence not merely over the question of the list of elements but into the study of chemistry generally. Disagreements over the relative weights to assign to different atoms led to disagreements over the number of atoms of particular elements within a given molecule.

Kekulé, shortly after he had published his suggestions leading to structural formulas, realized this concept would come to nothing if chemists could not agree, first of all, on empirical formulas. He therefore suggested a conference of important chemists from all over Europe to discuss the matter. As a result, an international scientific meeting was held for the first time in history. It was called the First International Chemical Congress, and it met in 1860 in the town of Karlsruhe, in Germany.

One hundred forty delegates attended, among them the Italian chemist Stanislao Cannizzaro (1826–1910). Two years earlier, Cannizzaro had come across the work of his countryman Avogadro (see page 82). He saw how Avogadro's hypothesis could be used to distinguish between the atomic weight and molecular weight of the important gaseous elements and how this distinction would serve to clarify the matter of atomic weights for the elements generally. Furthermore, he saw the importance of distinguishing carefully between atomic weight and equivalent weight.

At the Congress he made a strong speech on the subject and then distributed copies of a pamphlet in which he explained his points in full. Slowly and laboriously, he won over the chemical world to his views. From that time forward, the matter of atomic weight was clarified and the importance of Berzelius's table of atomic weights (see page 84) was appreciated.

In organic chemistry this development meant that men could now agree on empirical formulas and proceed onward to add detail in structural form, first in two dimensions, then in three. The manner in which this was done was described in the preceding chapter.

In inorganic chemistry, the results were just as fruitful, for there was now at least one rational order in which to arrange the elements–in order of increasing atomic weight. Once that was done, chemists could look at the list with fresh eyes.

Organizing the Elements

In 1864, the English chemist John Alexander Reina Newlands (1837–98) arranged the known elements in order of increasing atomic weights, and noted that this arrangement also placed the properties of the elements into at least a partial order. (See Figure 13.) When he arranged his elements into vertical columns of seven, similar elements tended to fall into the same horizontal rows. Thus, potassium fell next to the very similar sodium; selenium fell in the same row as the similar sulfur; calcium next to the similar magnesium, and so on. Indeed, each of Döbereiner's three triads were to be found among the rows.

Newlands called this the *law of octaves* (there are seven notes to an octave in music, the eighth note being almost a duplicate of the first note and beginning a new octave). Unfortunately, while some of the rows in his table did contain similar elements, other rows contained widely dissimilar elements. It was felt by other chemists that what Newlands was demonstrating was coincidence rather than some-

	No.		No.		No.		No.		No.		No.		No.		No.
H	1	F	8	Cl	15	Co Ni	22	Br	29	Pd	36	I	42	Pt Ir	50
Li	2	Na	9	K	16	Cu	23	Rb	30	Ag	37	Cs	44	Tl	53
Ga	3	Mg	10	Ca	17	Zn	25	Sr	31	Cd	38	Ba V	45	Pb	54
B	4	Al	11	Cr	19	Y	24	Ce La	33	U	40	Ta	46	Th	56
C	5	Si	12	Ti	18	In	26	Zr	32	Sn	39	W	47	Hg	52
N	6	P	13	Mn	20	As	27	Di Mo	34	Sb	41	Nb	48	Bi	55
O	7	S	14	Fe	21	Se	28	Ro Ru	35	Te	43	Au	49	Cs	51

FIG. 13. The "law of octaves," published in 1864 by J. A. R. Newlands, was a forerunner of Mendeléev's Periodic Table.

thing of significance. He failed to get his work published.

Two years earlier, a French geologist, Alexandre Emile Beguyer de Chancourtois (1820–86) had also arranged elements in order of increasing atomic weight and had plotted them on a sort of cylindrical graph. Here, too, similar elements tended to fall into vertical columns. He published his paper, but not his graph, and his work went unnoticed, too. (See Figure 14.)

More successful was the German chemist Julius Lothar Meyer (1830–95). Meyer considered the volume taken up by certain fixed weights of the various elements. Under such conditions, each weight contained the same number of atoms of its particular element. This meant that the ratio of the volumes of the various elements was equal to the ratio of the volumes of single atoms of the various elements. Therefore, one could speak of *atomic volumes*.

If the atomic volumes of the elements were plotted against the atomic weights, a series of waves was produced, rising to sharp peaks at the alkali metals: sodium, potassium, rubidium, and cesium. Each fall and rise to a peak corresponded to a *period* in the table of elements. In each period a number of physical properties other than atomic volume also fell and rose. (See Figure 15.)

Hydrogen, the first in the list of elements (it has the lowest atomic weight) is a special case and can be considered as making up the first period all by itself. The second and third period in Meyer's table included seven elements each, and duplicated Newlands's law of octaves. However, the two waves following included more than seven elements, and this clearly showed where Newlands had made his mistake. One could not force the law of octaves to hold strictly throughout the table of elements, with seven

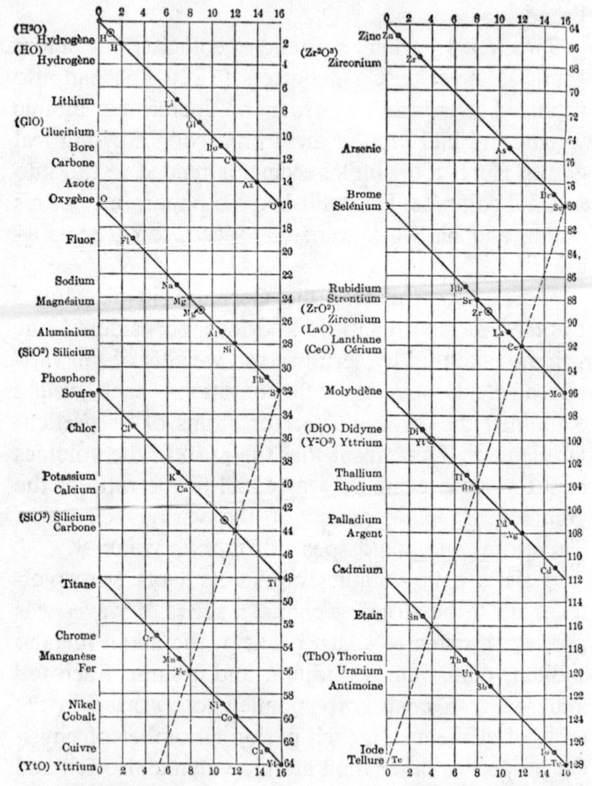

Nota.—On a entouré d'un cercle les pois correspondant aux caractères numériques dits *secondaires.*

FIG. 14. Spiral plot was the result when Beguyer de Chancourtois, in 1862, ordered the elements by atomic weight and related those with analogous properties.

elements in each row. The later periods had to be longer than the earlier periods.

Meyer published his work in 1870, but he was too late. The year before, a Russian chemist, Dmitri Ivanovich Mendeléev (1834–1907), had also discovered the change in length of the periods of ele-

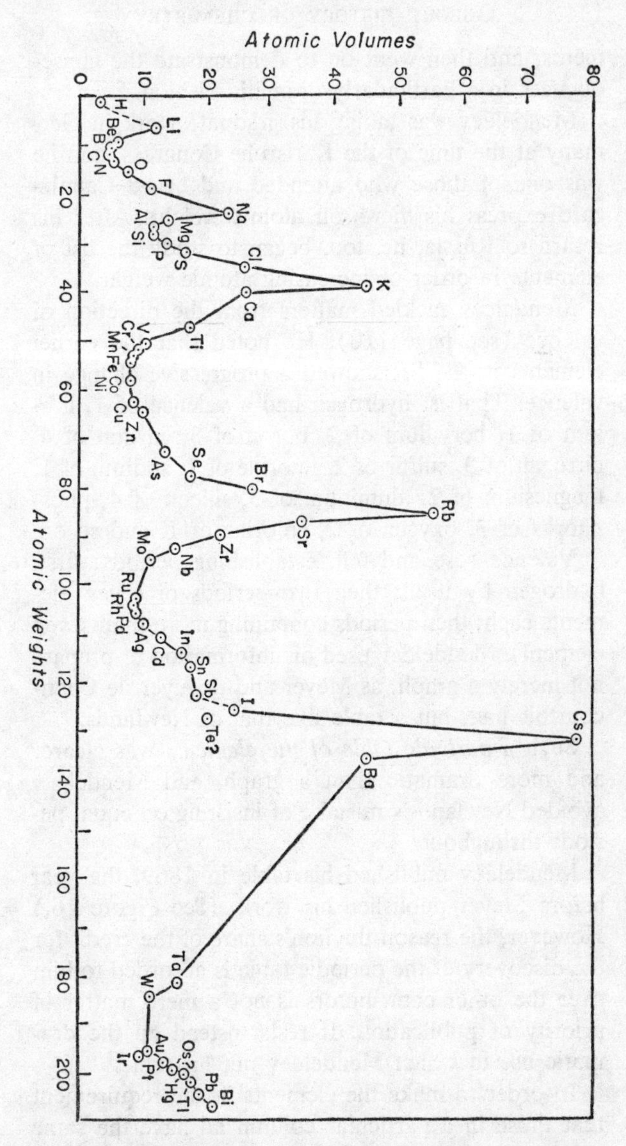

FIG. 15. Meyer's graph plotted fixed weights of elements against their volumes.

ments, and then went on to demonstrate the consequences in a particularly dramatic fashion.

Mendeléev was taking his graduate work in Germany at the time of the Karlsruhe Congress, and he was one of those who attended and heard Cannizzaro express his views on atomic weight. After his return to Russia, he, too, began to study the list of elements in order of increasing atomic weight.

Mendeléev tackled matters from the direction of valence (see page 110). He noted that the earlier elements in the list showed a progressive change in valence. That is, hydrogen had a valence of 1, lithium of 1, beryllium of 2, boron of 3, carbon of 4, nitrogen of 3, sulfur of 2, fluorine of 1, sodium of 1, magnesium of 2, aluminum of 3, silicon of 4, phosphorus of 3, oxygen of 2, chlorine of 1, and so on.

Valence rose and fell, establishing periods: first, hydrogen by itself; then two periods of seven elements each; then periods containing more than seven elements. Mendeléev used his information to prepare not merely a graph, as Meyer and Beguyer de Chancourtois had, but a table like that of Newlands.

Such a *periodic table of the elements* was clearer and more dramatic than a graph, and Mendeléev avoided Newlands's mistake of insisting on equal periods throughout.

Mendeléev published his table in 1869, the year before Meyer published his work. (See Figure 16.) However, the reason the lion's share of the credit for the discovery of the periodic table is accorded to him over the other contributors is not a mere matter of priority of publication. It rests instead on the dramatic use to which Mendeléev put his table.

In order to make the elements fit the requirement that those in a particular column all have the same valence, Mendeléev was forced in one or two cases to put an element of slightly higher atomic weight

но въ ней, мнѣ кажется, уже ясно выражается примѣнимость выставляемаго мною начала ко всей совокупности элементовъ, пай которыхъ извѣстенъ съ достовѣрностію. На этотъ разъ я и желалъ преимущественно найдти общую систему элементовъ. Вотъ этотъ опытъ:

			Ti=50	Zr=90	?=180.
			V=51	Nb=94	Ta=182.
			Cr=52	Mo=96	W=186.
			Mn=55	Rh=104,4	Pt=197,4
			Fe=56	Ru=104,4	Ir=198.
			Ni=Co=59	Pl=106,6,	Os=199.
H=1			Cu=63,4	Ag=108	Hg=200.
	Be=9,4	Mg=24	Zn=65,2	Cd=112	
	B=11	Al=27,4	?=68	Ur=116	Au=197?
	C=12	Si=28	?=70	Sn=118	
	N=14	P=31	As=75	Sb=122	Bi=210
	O=16	S=32	Se=79,4	Te=128?	
	F=19	Cl=35,5	Br=80	I=127	
Li=7	Na=23	K=39	Rb=85,4	Cs=133	Tl=204
		Ca=40	Sr=87,6	Ba=137	Pb=207.
		?=45	Ce=92		
		?Er=56	La=94		
		?Yt=60	Di=95		
		?In=75,6	Th=118?		

а потому приходится въ разныхъ рядахъ имѣть различное измѣненіе разностей, чего нѣтъ въ главныхъ числахъ предлагаемой таблицы. Или же придется предполагать при составленіи системы очень много недостающихъ членовъ. То и другое мало выгодно. Мнѣ кажется притомъ, наиболѣе естественнымъ составить кубическую систему (предлагаемая есть плоскостная), но и попытки для ея образованія не повели къ надлежащимъ результатамъ. Слѣдующія двѣ попытки могутъ показать то разнообразіе сопоставленій, какое возможно при допущеніи основнаго начала, высказаннаго въ этой статьѣ.

Li	Na	K	Cu	Rb	Ag	Cs	—	Tl
7	23	39	63,4	85,4	108	133		204
Be	Mg	Ca	Zn	Sr	Cd	Ba	—	Pb
B	Al	—	—	—	Ur	—	—	Bi?
C	Si	Ti	—	Zr	Sn	—	—	—
N	P	V	As	Nb	Sb	—	Ta	—
O	S	—	Se	—	Te	—	W	—
F	Cl	—	Br	—	J	—	—	—
19	35,5	58	80	190	127	160	190	220.

FIG. 16. First publication of Mendeléev's Periodic Table of the elements appeared in *Journal of the Russian Chemical Society* for 1869.

ahead of one of slightly lower atomic weight. Thus, tellurium (atomic weight 127.6, valence 2) had to be put ahead of iodine (atomic weight 126.9, valence 1) in order to keep tellurium in the valence-2 column and iodine in the valence-1 column.[1]

As if this were not enough, he also found it necessary to leave gaps altogether in his table. Rather than considering these gaps as imperfections in the table, Mendeléev seized upon them boldly as representing elements as yet undiscovered.

In 1871, he pointed to three gaps in particular, those falling next to the elements boron, aluminum, and silicon in the table as modified in that year. He went so far as to give names to the unknown elements that he insisted belonged in those gaps: *eka-boron, eka-aluminum,* and *eka-silicon* ("*eka*" is the Sanskrit word for "one"). He also predicted various properties of these missing elements, judging what these must be from the properties of the elements above and below the gaps in his table—thus following and completing the insight of Döbereiner.

The world of chemistry remained skeptical and would perhaps have continued so if Mendeléev's bold predictions had not been dramatically verified. That this happened was due, first of all, to use of a new chemical tool—the spectroscope.

Filling the Gaps

In 1814, a German optician, Joseph von Fraunhofer (1787–1826), was testing the excellent prisms he manufactured. He allowed light to pass first through a slit and then through his triangular glass prisms. The light, he found, formed a spectrum of

[1] Mendeléev's instinct in this respect led him aright, though the reason for it wasn't made clear for nearly half a century (see page 221).

color that was crossed by a series of dark lines. He counted some six hundred of these lines, carefully noting their positions.

These lines were made to yield startling information, in the late 1850s, by the German physicist Gustav Robert Kirchhoff (1824–87), working with the German chemist Robert Wilhelm Bunsen (1811–99).

The basic source of light they used was a *Bunsen burner*, invented by Bunsen and known to every beginning student in a chemistry laboratory down to this day. This device burns a mixture of gas and air to produce a hot, scarcely luminous flame. When Kirchhoff placed crystals of various chemicals in the flame, it glowed with light of particular colors. If this light was passed through a prism it separated into bright lines.

Each element, Kirchhoff showed, produced a characteristic pattern of bright lines when heated to incandescence, a pattern different from that of any other element. Kirchhoff had thus worked out a method of "fingerprinting" each element by the light it produced when heated. Once the elements had been fingerprinted, he could work backward and deduce the elements in an unknown crystal from the bright lines in its spectrum. The device used to analyze elements in this fashion was named the *spectroscope*. (See Figure 17.)

As we know today, light is produced as a result of certain events that occur within the atom. In each type of atom these events occur in a particular manner. Therefore, each element will emit light of certain wavelengths and no others.

If light falls upon vapor, those same events within the atoms of the vapor can be made to occur in reverse. Light of certain wavelengths is then absorbed rather than emitted. What's more, since the

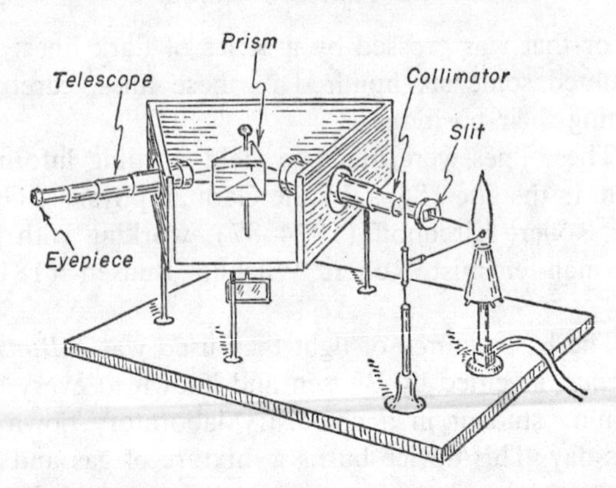

FIG. 17. Spectroscope, which was used in the discovery of several elements, enabled investigators to compare the bright-line spectra of incandescent metals.

same events are involved in either case (forward in one case, backward in the other), the wavelengths of light absorbed by vapor under one set of conditions are exactly the same as those that particular vapor would emit under another set of conditions.

The dark lines in the spectrum of sunlight were produced, it seemed very likely, by absorption of the light of the glowing body of the sun by the gases of its relatively cool atmosphere. The vapors in the sun's atmosphere absorbed light, and from the position of the resulting dark lines in the spectrum one could tell what elements were present in the sun's atmosphere.

The spectroscope was used to show that the sun (and the stars, too, as well as the gaseous material between the stars) was made up of elements identical with those on the earth. This conclusion finally exploded Aristotle's belief (see page 12) that the heavenly bodies consisted of substances distinct in nature from those making up the earth.

The spectroscope offered a new and powerful

method for detecting new elements. If a mineral brought to incandescence should reveal spectral lines belonging to no known element, it seemed reasonable to suppose that an unknown element was involved.

Bunsen and Kirchhoff proved this supposition handily when, in 1860, they tested a mineral with strange spectral lines and began to search it for a new element. They found the element and proved it to be an alkali metal, related in properties to sodium and potassium. They named it *cesium,* from a Latin word meaning "sky blue," for the color of the most prominent line in its spectrum. In 1861, they repeated their triumph by discovering still another alkali metal, *rubidium,* from a Latin word for red, again from the color of a spectral line.

Other chemists began to make use of this new tool. One of them was the French chemist Paul Emile Lecoq de Boisbaudran (1838–1912), who spent fifteen years studying the minerals of his native Pyrenees by means of the spectroscope. In 1875, he tracked down some unknown lines and found a new element in zinc ore. He named it *gallium,* for Gaul (France).

Sometime afterwards, he prepared enough of the new element to study its properties. Mendeléev read Lecoq de Boisbaudran's report and at once pointed out that the new element was none other than his own eka-aluminum. Further investigation made the identification certain; Mendeléev's prediction of the properties of eka-aluminum matched those of gallium in every respect.

The other two elements predicted by Mendeléev were found by older techniques. In 1879, a Swedish chemist, Lars Fredrick Nilson (1840–99), discovered a new element he called *scandium* (for Scandinavia). When its properties were reported, one of

Nilson's colleagues, the Swedish chemist Per Theodor Cleve (1840–1905), at once pointed out its similarity to Mendeléev's description of eka-boron.

Finally, in 1886, a German chemist, Clemens Alexander Winkler (1838–1904), analyzing a silver ore, found that all the known elements it contained amounted to only 93 per cent of its weight. Tracking down the remaining 7 per cent, he found a new element he called *germanium* (for Germany). This turned out to be Mendeléev's eka-silicon.

Thus, within fifteen years of Mendeléev's description of three missing elements, all three had been discovered and found to match his descriptions with amazing closeness. No one could doubt thereafter the validity or usefulness of the periodic table.

New Elements by Groups

Mendeléev's system had to withstand the impact of the discovery of still additional new elements, for which room might, or might not, be found in the periodic table.

As far back as 1794, for instance, a Finnish chemist, Johan Gadolin (1760–1852), had discovered a new metallic oxide (or *earth*) in a mineral obtained from the Ytterby quarry near Stockholm, Sweden. Because the new earth was much less common than such other earths as silica, lime, and magnesia, it was referred to as a *rare earth*. Gadolin named his oxide *yttria* after the quarry; fifty years later, it yielded the element *yttrium*. The rare earth minerals were analyzed during the mid-nineteenth century and were found to contain an entire group of new elements, the *rare earth elements*. The Swedish chemist Carl Gustav Mosander (1797–1858), for instance, discovered no fewer than four rare earth elements in the late 1830s and early 1840s. These were *lantha-*

num, erbium, terbium, and *didymium.* Actually, five were involved, for forty years later, in 1885, the Austrian chemist Carl Auer, Baron von Welsbach (1858–1929), found that didymium was a mixture of two elements, which he called *praseodymium* and *neodymium.* Lecoq de Boisbaudran discovered two others, *samarium,* in 1879, and *dysprosium,* in 1886. Cleve also discovered two: *holmium* and *thulium,* both in 1879. By 1907, when a French chemist, Georges Urbain (1872–1938), discovered the rare earth element *lutetium,* fourteen such elements in all had been discovered.

The rare earths possessed very similar chemical properties, and all had a valence of 3. One might suppose this meant they would all fall into a single column of the periodic table. Such an ordering, however, was impossible. No column was long enough to hold fourteen elements. Besides, the fourteen rare earth elements had a very closely spaced set of atomic weights. On the basis of the atomic weights they all had to be placed in a single horizontal row –in one period, in other words. Room could be made for them in the sixth period provided that period were assumed to be longer than the fourth and fifth periods, just as those were longer than the second and third. The similarity in properties of the rare earth elements went unexplained, however, until the 1920s (see page 248). Until then, the lack of explanation cast a shadow over the periodic table.

Another group of elements whose existence was completely unsuspected in Mendeléev's time caused no such trouble. Indeed, they fit into the periodic table beautifully.

Knowledge concerning them began with the work of the English physicist John William Strutt, Lord Rayleigh (1842–1919), who, in the 1880s, was working out with great care the atomic weights of oxygen, hydrogen, and nitrogen. In the case of nitrogen he found that the atomic weight varied according to the source of the gas. Nitrogen from the air seemed to have a slightly higher atomic weight than nitrogen from chemicals in the soil.

A Scottish chemist, William Ramsay (1852–1916), grew interested in this problem and recalled that Cavendish (see page 52), in a long-neglected experiment, had tried to combine the nitrogen of the air with oxygen. He had found that a final bubble of gas was left over which could not be made to combine with oxygen in any circumstances. That final bubble, then, could not have been nitrogen. Could it be that nitrogen, as ordinarily extracted from air, contained another gas, slightly denser than nitrogen, as an impurity, and that it was that gas which made nitrogen from air seem a little heavier than it ought to be?

In 1894, Ramsay repeated Cavendish's experiment and then applied an analytical instrument Cavendish had not possessed. Ramsay heated the final bubble of gas which would not react and studied the bright line of its spectrum. The strongest lines were in positions that fitted those of no known element. The final bubble was a new gas, then, denser than nitrogen and making up about 1 per cent of the volume of the atmosphere. It was chemically inert and could not be made to react with any other element, so it was named *argon,* from a Greek word meaning "inert."

Argon proved to have an atomic weight of just under 40. This meant that it would have to fit into the periodic table somewhere in the region of the following elements: sulfur (atomic weight 32), chlorine (atomic weight 35.5), potassium (atomic weight 39), and calcium (atomic weight, just over 40).

If the atomic weight of argon were the only thing to be considered, the new element would have to go between potassium and calcium. However, Mendeléev had established the principle that valence was more important than atomic weight (see page 134). Since argon combined with no element, it could be said to have a valence of 0. How did that fit?

The valence of sulfur is 2, that of chlorine 1, that of potassium 1, and that of calcium 2. The progression of valence in that region of the periodic table is 2,1,1,2. A valence of 0 would fit neatly between the two 1's: 2,1,0,1,2. Therefore argon was placed between chlorine and potassium.

However, if the periodic table was to be accepted as a guide, argon could not exist alone. It had to be one of a family of *inert gases,* each with a valence of 0. Such a family would fit neatly between the column containing the halogens (chlorine, bromine, etc.) and that containing the alkali metals (sodium, potassium, etc.), each with a valence of 1.

Ramsay began the search. In 1895, he learned that in the United States samples of a gas (that had been taken for nitrogen) had been obtained from a uranium mineral. Ramsay repeated the work and found that the gas, when tested spectroscopically, showed lines that belonged neither to nitrogen nor argon. Instead, most astonishingly, they were the lines that had been observed in the solar spectrum by the French astronomer Pierre Jules César Janssen (1824–1907) during a solar eclipse in 1868. At that time, the English astronomer Joseph Norman Lockyer (1836–1920) had attributed them to a new element which he had named *helium,* from a Greek word for sun.

On the whole, chemists had paid little attention at that time to a discovery of an unknown element in the sun based on evidence as fragile as a spectral

TYPE →	R_2O RH	RO RH_2	R_2O_3	RO_2	R_2O_5	RO_3	R_2O_7	RO_4			R_2O	RO	R_2O_3	RO_2 H_4R	R_2O_5 H_3R	RO_3 H_2R	R_2O_7 HR	
GROUP →	IA	IIA	IIIB	IVB	VB	VIB	VIIB	VIIIB			IB	IIB	IIIA	IVA	VA	VIA	VIIA	VIIIA
PERIOD 1	1 H HYDROGEN 1·0080																	INERT GASES 2 He HELIUM 4·003
	LIGHT METALS		HEAVY METALS										NONMETALS					
PERIOD 2	3 Li LITHIUM 6·940	4 Be BERYLLIUM 9·013											5 B BORON 10·82	6 C CARBON 12·011	7 N NITROGEN 14·008	8 O OXYGEN 16·000	9 F FLUORINE 19·000	10 Ne NEON 20·183
PERIOD 3	11 Na SODIUM 22·991	12 Mg MAGNESIUM 24·32											13 Al ALUMINUM 26·98	14 Si SILICON 28·09	15 P PHOSPHORUS 30·975	16 S SULFUR 32·066	17 Cl CHLORINE 35·457	18 A ARGON 39·944
PERIOD 4	19 K POTASSIUM 39·100	20 Ca CALCIUM 40·08	21 Sc SCANDIUM 45·10	22 Ti TITANIUM 47·90	23 V VANADIUM 50·95	24 Cr CHROMIUM 52·01	25 Mn MANGANESE 54·94	26 Fe IRON 55·85	27 Co COBALT 58·94	28 Ni NICKEL 58·71	29 Cu COPPER 63·54	30 Zn ZINC 65·38	31 Ga GALLIUM 69·72	32 Ge GERMANIUM 72·60	33 As ARSENIC 74·91	34 Se SELENIUM 78·96	35 Br BROMINE 79·916	36 Kr KRYPTON 83·80
PERIOD 5	37 Rb RUBIDIUM 85·48	38 Sr STRONTIUM 87·63	39 Y YTTRIUM 88·92	40 Zr ZIRCONIUM 91·22	41 Nb NIOBIUM 92·91	42 Mo MOLYBDENUM 95·95	43 Tc TECHNETIUM (99·)	44 Ru RUTHENIUM 101·1	45 Rh RHODIUM 102·91	45 Pd PALLADIUM 106·7	47 Ag SILVER 107·880	48 Cd CADMIUM 112·41	49 In INDIUM 114·76	50 Sn TIN 118·70	51 Sb ANTIMONY 121·76	52 Te TELLURIUM 127·61	53 I IODINE 126·91	54 Xe XENON 131·3
PERIOD 6	55 Cs CESIUM 132·91	56 Ba BARIUM 137·36	57–71 *	72 Hf HAFNIUM 178·58	73 Ta TANTALUM 180·95	74 W WOLFRAM 183·86	75 Re RHENIUM 186·22	76 Os OSMIUM 190·2	77 Ir IRIDIUM 192·2	78 Pt PLATINUM 195·23	79 Au GOLD 197·0	80 Hg MERCURY 200·61	81 Tl THALLIUM 204·39	82 Pb LEAD 207·21	83 Bi BISMUTH 209·00	84 Po POLONIUM 210·	85 At ASTATINE (211·)	86 Rn RADON 222·
PERIOD 7	87 Fr FRANCIUM (223·)	88 Ra RADIUM 226·05	89–98 **															

RARE EARTH ELEMENTS

*LANTHANIDE SERIES	57 La LANTHANUM 138·92	58 Ce CERIUM 140·13	59 Pr PRASEODYM-IUM 140·92	60 Nd NEODYMIUM 144·27	61 Pm PROMETHIUM (145·)	62 Sm SAMARIUM 150·35	63 Eu EUROPIUM 152·0	64 Gd GADOLINIUM 156·9	65 Tb TERBIUM 158·93	66 Dy DYSPROSIUM 162·51	67 Ho HOLMIUM 164·94	68 Er ERBIUM 167·27	69 Tm THULIUM 168·94	70 Yb YTTERBIUM 173·04	71 Lu LUTETIUM 174·99
** ACTINIDE SERIES	89 Ac ACTINIUM 227·0	90 Th THORIUM 232·15	91 Pa PROTACTIN-IUM 231·	92 U URANIUM 238·07	93 Np NEPTUNIUM (237)	94 Pu PLUTONIUM (242)	95 Am AMERICIUM (243)	96 Cm CURIUM (245)	97 Bk BERKELIUM (249)	98 Cf CALIFORNIUM (249)	99 E EINSTEINIUM (254)	100 Fm FERMIUM (252)	101 Mv MENDELEVIUM (256)	102 No NOBELIUM —	103? — —

FIG. 18. Modern Periodic Table orders elements by atomic number (the number of protons in the nucleus) and includes elements discovered since Mendeléev's day and those artificially produced since World War II.

line. But Ramsay's work showed the same element to exist on the earth, and he retained Lockyer's name. Helium is the lightest of the inert gases and, next to hydrogen, the element with the lowest atomic weight.

In 1898, Ramsay carefully boiled liquid air, looking for samples of inert gases that he expected to bubble off first. He found three, which he named *neon* ("new"), *krypton* ("hidden"), and *xenon* ("stranger").

The inert gases were at first considered mere curiosities, of interest only to the ivory-tower chemist. In researches beginning in 1910, however, the French chemist Georges Claude (1870–1960) showed that an electric current forced through certain gases such as neon produced a soft, colored light.

Tubes filled with such gas could be twisted into multi-colored letters of the alphabet, words, and designs. By the 1940s the incandescent light bulbs of New York City's celebrated Great White Way and similar centers of festivity had been replaced with *neon lights*.

CHAPTER 9

PHYSICAL CHEMISTRY

Heat

In the seventeenth and eighteenth centuries the worlds of chemistry and physics seemed well marked off from each other. Chemistry was the study of those changes that involved alterations in molecular structure. Physics was the study of those changes that did not involve such alterations.

In the early nineteenth century, while Davy (page 89) was altering the molecular arrangement of inorganic compounds and Berthelot (page 96) was altering the molecular arrangement of organic compounds, physicists were studying the flow of heat. This study of the flow of heat is called *thermodynamics* (from Greek words for "heat movement").

Prominent in this field were the English physicist James Prescott Joule (1818–89) and the German physicists Julius Robert von Mayer (1814–78) and Hermann Ludwig Ferdinand von Helmholtz (1821–94). By the 1840s their work made it clear that in the vicissitudes undergone by heat and other forms of energy, no energy was either created or destroyed. This principle is called the *law of conservation of energy* or the *first law of thermodynamics.*

The work of the French physicist Nicolas Léonard Sadi Carnot (1796–1832), the English physicist William Thomson, later Lord Kelvin (1824–

1907), and the German physicist Rudolf Julius Emanuel Clausius (1822–88) went further. It was shown that, left to itself, heat flowed spontaneously from a point at higher temperature to one of lower temperature, and that work could be obtained from heat only when such a heat flow across a temperature-difference existed. This inference could be generalized to apply to any form of energy flowing from a point of higher intensity to one of lower.

Clausius, in 1850, invented the term *entropy* for the ratio of the heat content of an isolated system to its absolute temperature. He showed that in any spontaneous energy change the entropy of the system would increase. This principle is called the *second law of thermodynamics.*

But this sort of advance in physics could not be isolated from chemistry. After all, apart from the sun, the major sources of heat in the nineteenth century world lay in chemical reactions such as the burning of wood, coal, or oil.

Other chemical reactions also evolved heat, the neutralization of acids by bases, for instance (see page 70). In fact, all chemical reactions involved some sort of heat transfer, either the emission of heat (and sometimes light) to the outside world, or the absorption of heat (and sometimes light) from the outside world.

It was in 1840 that the worlds of physics and chemistry met and began to fuse in the work of a Swiss-Russian chemist, Germain Henri Hess (1802–50). He announced the results of careful measurements he had made of the actual quantity of heat evolved in the chemical reactions, of fixed quantities of some substances. He was able to demonstrate that the quantity of heat produced (or absorbed) in going from one substance to another was the same no matter by what chemical route the change occurred, or in how many stages. Because of this generalization (*Hess's law*), Hess is sometimes considered the founder of *thermochemistry* (heat-chemistry).

Hess's law made it seem highly likely that the law of conservation of energy applied to chemical changes as well as to physical changes. Indeed, to generalize further, the laws of thermodynamics very likely held in chemistry as in physics.

This line of experiment and reasoning made it seem that chemical reactions, like physical processes, had an inherent spontaneous direction in which entropy was increased. Entropy is a difficult quantity to measure directly, however, and chemists sought other and simpler criteria that would serve as the measure of the "driving force."

In the 1860s, Berthelot, who had done such important work in organic synthesis (see page 96), turned to thermochemistry. He devised methods for conducting chemical reactions within a closed chamber surrounded by water at known temperature. From the rise in the temperature of the surrounding water at the conclusion of the reaction, the quantity of heat evolved by the reaction could be measured.

Using such a *calorimeter* (from the Latin for heat-measure), Berthelot ran careful determinations of the quantity of heat evolved by hundreds of different chemical reactions. Independently, the Danish chemist Hans Peter Jörgen Julius Thomsen (1826–1909) did similar experiments.

Berthelot felt that reactions that give off heat were spontaneous, while those that absorbed heat were not. Since every reaction that gave off heat had to absorb heat when forced into reverse (Lavoisier and Laplace, see page 62, were the first to hold such views), this meant that any chemical reaction would move spontaneously in only one direction and would give off heat while doing so.

As an example, when hydrogen and oxygen combine to form water, the reaction gives off a great deal of heat. This reaction is spontaneous, and, once started, goes rapidly to completion—sometimes with explosive violence.

The reverse reaction, however, that of water breaking down into hydrogen and oxygen, requires an input of energy. The energy may be in the form of heat, or, better yet, of electricity. However, such a breakdown of the water molecule is not spontaneous. It does not seem to occur at all until energy is supplied and, even then, the reaction ceases the moment the energy input is interrupted.

But Berthelot's generalization, however plausible it seems on the surface, is flawed. In the first place, not all spontaneous reactions give off heat. Some absorb heat so that, as they proceed, the temperature of the surroundings actually drops.

Secondly, there are *reversible reactions*. In these, Substances A and B can react spontaneously and be converted to Substances C and D, while C and D can, just as spontaneously, react back to A and B. And all this happens despite the fact that if heat is given off in the reaction occurring in one direction it must be absorbed in the reverse reaction. A simple example is that of hydrogen iodide, which breaks down to a mixture of hydrogen and iodine. The mixture is capable of recombining to hydrogen iodide. This can be written in equation form: $2HI \rightleftarrows H_2 + I_2$. The double arrow indicates a reversible reaction.

Reversible reactions were already known in Berthelot's time. They were first carefully studied, in 1850, by Williamson in the course of the work which led to his conclusions concerning ethers (see page 108). He found situations in which, beginning with a mixture of A and B, the substances C and D were formed. If he began instead with a mixture of C and

D, substances A and B were formed. In either case, there would be a mixture of A, B, C, and D in the end, with the proportions apparently fixed. The mixture would be at an *equilibrium.*

Williamson, however, did not believe that because the composition of the mixture was apparently fixed, nothing was happening. He felt that A and B were reacting to C and D, while C and D were reacting to A and B. Both reactions were in constant progress but neutralized each other's effects, giving the illusion of rest. This condition was *dynamic equilibrium.*

Williamson's work marked the beginning of the study of *chemical kinetics*–the study of the rates of chemical reactions. It was quite evident from Williamson's work that something more than the mere evolution of heat dictated the spontaneity of a chemical reaction. This "something more" was already being worked out while Berthelot and Thomsen were making their numerous calorimetric measurements but, unfortunately, the matter remained buried in a little-known tongue.

Chemical Thermodynamics

In 1863, the Norwegian chemists Cato Maximilian Guldberg (1836–1902) and Peter Waage (1833–1900) published a pamphlet dealing with the direction of spontaneous reactions. They returned to a suggestion made half a century before by Berthollet (see page 64), that the direction taken by a reaction depended upon the mass of the individual substances taking part in the reaction.

To Guldberg and Waage, it seemed that mass alone was not the entire answer. Rather it was a question of the amount of mass of a particular substance crowded into a given volume of the reacting mixture, on the *concentration* of the substance, in other words.

Suppose A and B can react to form C and D, while C and D can react to form A and B. This double reaction can be represented as follows:

$$A+B \rightleftarrows C+D$$

The situation symbolized is an example of one of Williamson's reversible reactions, and it reaches an equilibrium under conditions in which A, B, C, and D all exist in the system. The point of equilibrium depends on the rate at which A and B react (rate 1) as compared with that at which C and D react (rate 2).

Suppose rate 1 is much higher than rate 2. In that case, A and B are reacting quickly, producing a considerable quantity of C and D; while C and D react slowly and produce a small amount of A and B. Before long, most of the A and B has changed over to C and D and little has changed back. When the reaction reaches equilibrium, then, C and D dominate the mixture. Looking at the equation just above, we would say that the equilibrium point is "far to the right."

The reverse is true when rate 2 is much higher than rate 1. In that case, C and D would react to produce A and B much more quickly than A and B would react to produce C and D. At equilibrium, A and B would dominate the mixture. The equilibrium point is then "far to the left."

But rate 1 depends on how frequently a molecule of A happens to collide with a molecule of B, for only upon such a collision can reaction occur, and not always even then. Again, rate 2 depends on how frequently a molecule of C collides with a molecule of D.

Suppose, then, that additional A or B (or both)

is added to the system without changing its volume. The concentration of A or B (or both) is increased and there is now a greater likelihood of collisions among them (just as there is a greater likelihood of automobile collisions when a highway is crowded at rush hour than when it is relatively empty at mid-morning).

Increasing the concentration of A or B or both thus increases rate 1; decreasing the concentration will decrease the rate. Similarly, an increase in the concentration of C or D or both, will increase the concentration of rate 2. By altering rate 1, or rate 2, one can alter the composition of the equilibrium mixture. If the concentration of any of the participating substances is altered, therefore, the position of the equilibrium point is changed.

Though the concentrations of A, B, C, and D at equilibrium would shift as one or more of these components were added to or taken from the mixture, Guldberg and Waage found they could cling to one unchanging factor. The ratio of the product of the concentrations of the substances on one side of the double arrow to the product of the concentrations on the other side of the double arrow, at equilibrium, remains constant.

Suppose we represent the concentration of a given substance by placing brackets about its symbol. We can say, then, in connection with the reaction we have been discussing, that, at equilibrium:

$$\frac{[C][D]}{[A][B]} = K$$

The symbol, K, represents the *equilibrium constant,* which is characteristic for any given reversible reaction being run at a fixed temperature.

Guildberg and Waage's *law of mass action* was an

adequate guide to the understanding of reversible reactions, much more so than Berthelot's fallacious suggestion. Unfortunately, Guldberg and Waage published in Norwegian, and their work went unnoticed until 1879, when it was translated into German.

In the meantime, an American physicist, Josiah Willard Gibbs (1839–1903), was systematically applying the laws of thermodynamics to chemical reactions. He published a number of long papers on the subject between 1876 and 1878.

Gibbs evolved the notion of *free energy,* a quantity which incorporated within itself both heat content and entropy. When a chemical reaction occurred, the free energy of the system changed. When the free energy decreased, the entropy always increased, and the reaction was spontaneous. (The value of the free energy lay in the fact that its change was easier to measure than the change in entropy.) The change in heat content depended on the exact amount by which free energy decreased and entropy increased. Usually, the heat content also decreased in a spontaneous reaction so that heat was given off. Occasionally, though, the change in free energy and entropy was such that the heat content increased and then a reaction, though spontaneous, absorbed energy.

Gibbs also showed that the free energy of a system changed somewhat with changes in the concentration of the chemicals making up that system. Suppose that the free energy of $A + B$ is not much different from that of $C + D$. Then, the small changes introduced by changes in concentration might be enough to make the free energy of $A + B$ more than that of $C + D$ at some concentrations and less at others. The reaction could move spontaneously in one direction at one set of concentrations and in the opposite direction (but just as spontaneously) at another set.

The rate at which free energy changes as the concentration of a particular substance changes is the *chemical potential* of that substance, and Gibbs could show that it was the chemical potential that acted as the "driving force" behind chemical reactions. A chemical reaction moved spontaneously from a point of high chemical potential to one of low, as heat flowed spontaneously from a point of high temperature to one of low.

In this way, Gibbs gave meaning to the law of mass action for he showed that at equilibrium the sum of the chemical potentials of all the substances involved was at a minimum. If one began with A + B, it moved down the chemical potential "hill" as C + D was formed. If one began with C + D, it moved downward as A + B was formed. At equilibrium, the bottom of the "energy valley" between the two "hills" had been reached.

Gibbs went on to apply thermodynamic principles to equilibria between different phases (liquid, solid, and gas) included within a particular chemical system. For instance, liquid water and water vapor (one component, two phases) could exist together at different temperatures and pressures, but if the temperature was fixed, the pressure was fixed also. Liquid water, water vapor, and ice (one component, three phases) could exist all together at only one particular temperature and pressure.

Gibbs worked out a simple equation, the *phase rule,* which enabled one to predict the manner in which temperature, pressure, and the concentrations of various components could be varied under all combinations of components and phases.

Thus was founded *chemical thermodynamics* in such detail and with such thoroughness that little was left to be done by those who came after Gibbs.[1] Nevertheless, despite the fundamental importance and remarkable elegance of Gibbs's work, it did not at once receive recognition in Europe, since it was published in an American journal that was ignored by the European leaders in the field.

Catalysis

In the final quarter of the nineteenth century, Germany was leading the world in the study of the physical changes associated with chemical reactions. The outstanding worker in this field of *physical chemistry* was the Russian-German chemist Friedrich Wilhelm Ostwald (1853–1932). It was thanks to him, more than to any other individual, that physical chemistry came to be recognized as a discipline in its own right. By 1887, he had written the first textbook on the subject and founded the first journal to be devoted exclusively to the field.

Fittingly enough, Ostwald was among the first Europeans to discover and appreciate Gibbs's work. He translated Gibbs's papers on chemical thermodynamics into German in 1892. Ostwald proceeded to put Gibbs's theories to use almost at once in connection with the phenomenon of *catalysis*.

Catalysis (a word suggested by Berzelius in 1835)

[1] An example of one important addition, however, was that introduced by the American chemist Gilbert Newton Lewis (1875–1946). In 1923, in a classic book on thermodynamics, he introduced the concept of *activity*. The activity of a substance is not identical with its concentration but is related to it. The equations of chemical thermodynamics can be made more accurate over a wider range, if activity is substituted for concentration.

is a process whereby the rate of a particular chemical reaction is hastened, sometimes enormously so, by the presence of small quantities of a substance which does not itself seem to take part in the reaction. Thus, powdered platinum will catalyze the addition of hydrogen to oxygen and to a variety of organic compounds, as Davy (the isolator of sodium and potassium) discovered in 1816. Again, acid will catalyze the breakdown to simpler units of a number of organic compounds, as G. S. Kirchhoff first showed in 1812 (see page 97). At the conclusion of the reaction, the platinum or the acid is still present in its original quantity.

Ostwald prepared, in 1894, a summary of someone else's paper on the heat of combustion of foods, this summary to appear in his own journal. He disagreed strongly with the conclusions of the writer, and to buttress his disagreement discussed catalysis.

He pointed out that the theories of Gibbs made it necessary to assume that catalysts hastened reactions without altering the energy relationships of the substances involved. The catalyst, he maintained, must combine with the reacting substance to form an intermediate that breaks up to give the final products. The breakup of the intermediate released the catalyst, which thus resumed its original form.

Without the presence of this catalyst-combined intermediate, the reaction would proceed much more slowly, sometimes so slowly as to be imperceptible. Hence, the effect of the catalyst was to hasten the reaction without itself being consumed. Furthermore, since a molecule of catalyst was used over and over, a small quantity of catalyst was sufficient to hasten a great deal of reaction.

This view of catalysis is still held today. It has helped to explain the activity of the protein catalysts (or *enzymes*) which control the chemical reactions in living tissue.[2]

Ostwald was a follower of the principles of the Austrian physicist and philosopher Ernst Mach (1838–1916), who believed that scientists should deal only with matters that could be directly measured, and should not create "models" based only on indirect evidence. For this reason, Ostwald refused to accept the reality of atoms, since there was no direct evidence for their existence. He was the last important scientist to resist the atomic theory (though he did not deny its usefulness, of course).

Here, however, the matter of Brownian motion came up. This phenomenon, involving the rapid, irregular motion of small particles suspended in water, was first observed (in 1827) by a Scottish botanist, Robert Brown (1773–1858).

The German-Swiss physicist Albert Einstein (1879–1955) showed, in 1905, that this motion could be attributed to the bombardment of the particle by molecules of water. Since, at any given moment, more molecules might be striking from one direction than from the other, the particles would be pushed now here, now there. Einstein worked out an equation which could be used to calculate the actual size of the water molecules once certain properties of the moving particles were measured.

A French physicist, Jean Baptiste Perrin (1870–1942), made the necessary measurements in 1908 and produced the first hard and fast estimate of the diameter of molecules and, therefore, of atoms. Since the Brownian motion was a reasonably direct

[2] The growth of knowledge in the field of *biochemistry* (that is, the chemical reactions, usually enzyme-controlled, that proceed in living tissue) is taken up only glancingly in this book. It is discussed in greater detail in my book *A Short History of Biology*.

observation of the effects of individual molecules, even Ostwald had to abandon his opposition to the atomic theory.[3]

Nor was Ostwald the only one in the 1890s to recognize the worth of Gibbs. The Dutch physical chemist, Hendrik Willem Bakhuis Roozeboom (1854–1907), publicized Gibbs's phase rule throughout Europe and did so most effectively.

Then, too, Gibbs's work was translated into French in 1899 by Henri Louis Le Chatelier (1850–1936). Le Chatelier, a physical chemist, is best known today for his enunciation of a rule, in 1888, that is still called *Le Chatelier's principle.* This rule may be stated: Every change of one of the factors of an equilibrium brings about a rearrangement of the system in such a direction as to minimize the original change.

In other words, if a system in equilibrium is placed under increased pressure, it rearranges itself so as to take up as little room as possible and thus decrease the pressure. If the temperature is raised, it undergoes a change that absorbs heat and lowers the temperature and so on. As it turned out, Gibbs's chemical thermodynamics explained Le Chatelier's principle neatly.

The late discovery of Gibbs by Europeans did not delay the development of physical chemistry as much as it might have, for many of Gibbs's findings were

[3] Evidence in favor of the existence of atoms (about 1/250,000,000 of an inch in diameter) and even smaller particles has continued to pile up in overwhelming amount since Perrin's time. Some of this evidence will be detailed in the last three chapters of this book. As a climax to the story that began with Democritus (see page 13), the German-American physicist Erwin Wilhelm Mueller (1911–   ) has invented a *field-emission microscope.* In the mid-1950s photographs were taken with it which have already become classics and which actually made visible the arrangement of individual atoms in the tip of a metallic needle.

worked out independently, during the 1880s, by Van't Hoff, who had previously presented the world of chemistry with the tetrahedral carbon atom (see page 119).

Van't Hoff was second only to Ostwald as an important worker in the field of physical chemistry. He worked on the problems of solutions in particular. By 1886 he was able to show that the molecules of dissolved substances, moving randomly through the body of the liquid in which they were dissolved, behaved, in some ways, according to rules analogous to those which described the behavior of gases.

Nor did the new study of physical chemistry connect chemical reactions with heat alone; it was rather with energy generally. Electricity, for instance, could be produced by chemical reactions and could in turn bring about chemical reactions.

Walther Hermann Nernst, a German (1864–1941), applied the principles of thermodynamics to the chemical reactions proceeding in a battery. In 1889, he showed how the characteristics of the current produced could be used to calculate the free energy change in the chemical reaction producing the current.

Light was still another form of energy that could be produced in a chemical reaction and, as was discovered even before the nineteenth century, it could in turn induce chemical reactions. In particular, light could break down certain silver compounds, liberating black grains of metallic silver. The study of such light-induced reactions is termed *photochemistry* ("light-chemistry").

In the 1830s, the action of light on silver had been developed into a technique for allowing sunlight to paint a picture. A layer of silver compound upon a glass plate (later, upon a flexible film) is briefly exposed, by way of a focusing lens, to a sunlit scene. Different areas of the silver compound are exposed to different amounts of light, according to how much was reflected from this point or that point in the scene. The brief exposure to the light increases the tendency of the silver compound to break down to metallic silver; the brighter the light, the more sharply increased the tendency.

The silver compound is then treated with chemicals that bring about such a breakdown to metallic silver. The region exposed to bright light completes the breakdown much more rapidly. If the "development" is stopped at the right point, the glass plate is covered by a pattern of dark (silver grains) and light (unchanged silver compound) that complements the pattern of the original scene.

Through further optical and chemical processes that need not be described here, a realistic portrayal of the scene is eventually obtained. The process is termed *photography* ("light-writing"). A number of men contributed to the new technique, including the French physicist Joseph Nicéphore Niepce (1765–1833), the French artist Louis Jacques Mandé Daguerre (1789–1851), and the English inventor William Henry Fox Talbot (1800–77).

Particularly interesting, though, was the manner in which light behaved almost as a catalyst. A small quantity of light could induce a mixture of hydrogen and chlorine to react with explosive violence where, in the dark, no reaction at all would occur.

The explanation for this drastic difference in behavior was finally advanced by Nernst in 1918. A small quantity of light suffices to break the chlorine molecule apart into two single chlorine atoms. One chlorine atom (much more active in itself than as part of a molecule) snatches a hydrogen atom from the hydrogen molecule, to form a hydrogen chloride molecule. The remaining hydrogen atom, isolated, snatches a chlorine from a chlorine molecule; the remaining chlorine atom snatches a hydrogen from a hydrogen molecule, and so on.

The original bit of light is thus responsible for a photochemical *chain reaction,* which leads to the formation of a great many hydrogen chloride molecules at an explosive rate.

Ionic Dissociation

Added to Ostwald and Van't Hoff was another master of early physical chemistry, the Swedish chemist Svante August Arrhenius (1859–1927). As a student, Arrhenius turned his attention to electrolytes; that is, to those solutions capable of carrying an electric current.

Faraday had worked out the laws of electrolysis, and from those laws it had seemed that electricity, like matter, might well exist in the form of tiny particles (see page 90). Faraday had spoken of ions, which might be considered as particles carrying electricity through a solution. For the next half century, however, neither he nor anyone else had ventured to work seriously on what the nature of those ions might be. This did not mean, however, that no valuable work was done. In 1853, the German physicist Johann Wilhelm Hittorf (1824–1914) pointed out that some ions traveled more rapidly than others. This observation led to the concept of *transport number,* the rate at which particular ions carried the electric current. But even calculation of this rate still left the nature of ions an open question.

Arrhenius found his entry into the field through the work of the French chemist François Marie Raoult (1830–1901). Like Van't Hoff, Raoult studied solutions. His studies were climaxed in 1887 with his establishment of what is now called *Raoult's law:*

The partial pressure of solvent vapor in equilibrium with a solution is directly proportional to the mole fraction of the solvent.

Without going into the definition of mole fraction, it is sufficient to say that this rule made it possible to estimate the relative number of particles (whether of atoms, molecules or the mysterious ions) of the substance which is dissolved (the *solute*) and of the liquid in which it is dissolved (the *solvent*).

In the course of this research, Raoult had measured the freezing points of solutions. Such freezing points were always "depressed"; that is, were lower than the freezing point of the pure solvent. Raoult was able to show that the freezing point was depressed in proportion to the number of particles of solute present in the solution.

But here a problem was created. It was reasonable to suppose that when a substance dissolved in, let us say, water it broke up into separate molecules. Sure enough, in the case of non-electrolytes such as sugar, the depression of the freezing point fit that assumption. However, when an electrolyte like common salt (NaCl) was dissolved, the depression of the freezing point was twice as great as it should have been. The number of particles present was twice the number of salt molecules. If barium chloride ($BaCl_2$) was dissolved, the number of particles present was three times as great as the number of molecules.

A molecule of sodium chloride is made up of two atoms, and a molecule of barium chloride is made up of three atoms. It seemed to Arrhenius, then, that when certain molecules were dissolved in a solvent such as water, those molecules broke down into the individual atoms. Furthermore, since those molecules, once broken down, conducted an electric current (whereas molecules such as sugar, which did not break apart, did not carry an electric current), Arrhenius further suggested that the molecules did not break down (or "dissociate") into ordinary atoms, but into atoms carrying an electric charge.

Faraday's ions, Arrhenius proposed, were simply atoms (or groups of atoms) carrying either a positive or a negative electric charge. The ions were either the "atoms of electricity" or they carried those "atoms of electricity." (The latter alternative eventually proved correct.) Arrhenius used his theory of *ionic dissociation* to account for many facts of electrochemistry.

Arrhenius's ideas, advanced as his Ph.D. thesis in 1884, met with considerable resistance; his thesis was almost rejected. However, Ostwald, impressed, offered Arrhenius a position and encouraged him to continue work in physical chemistry.

In 1889, Arrhenius made another fruitful suggestion. He pointed out that molecules, on colliding, need not react unless they collided with a certain minimum energy, an *energy of activation*. When this energy of activation is low, reactions proceed quickly and smoothly. A high energy of activation, however, might keep a reaction from proceeding at more than an infinitesimal rate.

If, in the latter case, the temperature were raised, however, so that a number of molecules received the necessary energy of activation, the reaction would then proceed suddenly and quickly, sometimes with explosive violence. The explosion of a hydrogen-oxygen mixture when the *ignition temperature* is reached is an example.

Ostwald used this concept profitably in working out his theory of catalysis. He pointed out that the formation of a catalyst-combined intermediate (see page 156) required a smaller energy of activation than the direct formation of the final products required.

More on Gases

The properties of gases came under new and refined scrutiny during the burgeoning of physical chemistry in the late nineteenth century. Three centuries earlier, Boyle had advanced Boyle's law (see page 38), stating that the pressure and volume of a given quantity of gas varied inversely (provided, as was later shown, that temperature is held constant).

This law turned out, however, to be not exactly true. The German-French chemist Henri Victor Regnault (1810–78) made many careful measurements of gas volumes and pressures in the mid-nineteenth century and showed that, especially as pressure was raised or temperature was lowered, gases did not quite follow Boyle's law.

At about the same time, the Scottish physicist James Clerk Maxwell (1831–79) and the Austrian physicist Ludwig Boltzmann (1844–1906) had analyzed the behavior of gases on the assumption that they were an assemblage of a vast number of randomly moving particles (the *kinetic theory of gases*). They were able to derive Boyle's law on this basis, provided they made two further assumptions: 1. that there were no attractive forces between gas molecules, and 2. that the gas molecules were of zero size. Gases that fulfill these assumptions are *perfect gases.*

Neither assumption is quite correct. There are small attractions between gas molecules, and though these molecules are exceedingly small, their size is not zero. No actual gas is quite "perfect," therefore, although hydrogen and the later-discovered helium (see page 143) come close.

Taking these facts into account, the Dutch physicist Johannes Diderik Van der Waals (1837–1923), in 1873, worked out an equation that related pressure, volume, and temperature of gases. This equation included two constants, *a* and *b* (different for each gas), the existence of which allowed for the size of the molecules and the attractions among them.

The better understanding of the properties of gases helped to solve the problem of liquefying them.

As early as 1799, the gas ammonia was liquefied by being cooled while it was under pressure. (Raising the pressure raises the temperature at which a gas will liquefy and makes the liquefaction process that much easier.) Faraday was particularly active in this field of investigation, and by 1845 had been able to liquefy a number of gases, chlorine and sulfur dioxide among them. Once a liquefied gas is released from pressure, it begins to evaporate rapidly. The process of evaporation absorbs heat, however, and the temperature of the remaining liquid drops drastically. Liquid carbon dioxide will under such conditions freeze to solid carbon dioxide. By mixing solid carbon dioxide with ether, Faraday could obtain temperatures of −78° C.

Foiling his best efforts, however, were such gases as oxygen, nitrogen, hydrogen, carbon monoxide, and methane. No matter how high the pressures he worked at, Faraday could not liquefy them. These substances came to be termed "permanent gases."

In the 1860s, however, an Irish chemist, Thomas Andrews (1813–85), was working with carbon dioxide which he had liquefied by pressure alone. Slowly raising the temperature, he noted the manner in which the pressure had to be increased to keep the carbon dioxide in the liquid state. He found that at a temperature of 31° C., no amount of pressure sufficed. At that temperature, in fact, the gas and liquid phase seemed to melt together, so to speak, and become indistinguishable. Therefore, Andrews suggested (in 1869) that for each gas there was a *critical temperature,* above which no amount of pressure alone could liquefy it. It followed that permanent gases were simply those with critical temperatures well below those reached in the laboratories.

Meanwhile, Joule and Thomson (see page 148) in their studies on heat had discovered that gases could be cooled by allowing them to expand. If, therefore, gases were allowed to expand, then compressed under conditions which did not allow them to regain the lost heat, and expanded once more, and so on over and over, then very low temperatures could be achieved. Once a temperature below the critical temperature for that gas was reached, application of pressure would liquefy it.

Using this technique, the French physicist Louis Paul Cailletet (1832–1913) and the Swiss chemist Raoul Pictet (1846–1929) were able to liquefy such gases as oxygen, nitrogen, and carbon monoxide by 1877. Hydrogen, however, still balked their efforts.

As a result of Van der Waals's work, it became clear that in the case of hydrogen the Joule-Thomson effect would work only below a certain temperature. Its temperature had to be lowered, therefore, before the cycle of expansion and contraction could be started.

In the 1890s, the Scottish chemist James Dewar (1842–1923) began work on the problem. He prepared liquid oxygen in quantity and stored it in a *Dewar flask.* This is a double-walled flask with a vacuum between the walls. The vacuum will not transmit heat by conduction or convection, since both phenomena require the presence of matter. Heat is transmitted across a vacuum only by the comparatively slow process of radiation. By silvering the walls so that radiated heat would be reflected rather than absorbed, Dewar slowed down that process even further. (The household thermos flask is simply a Dewar flask with a stopper.)

Hydrogen gas could be cooled to very low temperatures by immersion in liquid oxygen kept in such flasks, and the Joule-Thomson effect could then be made use of. As a result, Dewar produced liquid hydrogen in 1898.

Hydrogen liquefied at 20° K., a temperature but twenty degrees above absolute zero.[4] This is not a record low liquefaction point, by any means. In the 1890s, the inert gases had been discovered (see page 147), and one of these, helium, liquefied at a still lower temperature.

The Dutch physicist Heike Kamerlingh Onnes (1853–1926) overcame the last obstacle when, in 1908, he cooled helium first in a bath of liquid hydrogen, then applied the Joule-Thomson effect. He produced liquid helium at a temperature of 4° K.

[4] The concept of *absolute zero,* the lowest temperature possible, was first advanced by Thomson (Lord Kelvin) in 1848. In recognition of this proposal, the absolute temperature scale (based on Kelvin's concept) is symbolized as °K. In 1905, Nernst showed that entropy was zero at absolute zero (the *third law of thermodynamics*). From this, one could deduce that though a temperature of absolute zero could be approached as closely as desired, it could never actually be reached.

CHAPTER 10

SYNTHETIC ORGANIC CHEMISTRY

Dyes

When, in the first half of the nineteenth century, men like Berthelot (page 96) began to put together organic molecules, they were extending drastically the accepted limits of their science. Instead of confining their investigations to the existing physical environment, they were beginning to imitate the creativity of nature, and it was to be only a matter of time until nature would be surpassed. In a very small way, Berthelot's work with some of his synthetic fats was a start in this direction, but much more remained to be done.

Insufficient understanding of molecular structure hampered the organic chemists of the mid-nineteenth century, but such was the irresistible progress of the science that in at least one significant episode even this shortcoming actually turned out to be an advantage.

At the time (the 1840s) there were few organic chemists of note in Great Britain, and August Wilhelm von Hofmann (1818–92), who had worked under Liebig (page 102), was imported to London from Germany. For an assistant, some years later, Hofmann drew a teen-age student, William Henry Perkin (1838–1907). One day, in Perkin's presence, Hofmann speculated aloud on the feasibility of synthesizing quinine, the valuable anti-malarial. Hofmann had done research on chemicals obtained from coal tar (a thick, black liquid obtained by heating coal in the absence of air), and he wondered whether it was possible to synthesize quinine from a coal tar chemical like aniline. The synthesis, if it could be accomplished, would be a great stroke, he said; it would relieve Europe's dependence on the far-off tropics for the supply of quinine.

Perkin, all on fire, went home (where he had a small laboratory of his own) to tackle the job. Had he or Hofmann known more of the structure of the quinine molecule, they would have known the task was impossible to mid-nineteenth century techniques. Fortunately, Perkin was blissfully ignorant of this and, though he failed, he achieved something perhaps greater.

During the Easter vacation in 1856, he had treated aniline with potassium dichromate and was about to discard the resulting mess as just another failure when his eye caught a purplish glint in the material. He added alcohol, which dissolved something out of the mess and turned a beautiful purple.

Perkin suspected he had a dye. He left school and used family money to start a factory. Within six months, he was producing what he called "Aniline Purple." French dyers clamored for the new dye and named the color "mauve." So popular did the color become that this period of history is known as the Mauve Decade. Perkin, having founded the huge *synthetic dye* industry, could retire, wealthy, at thirty-five.

It was not long after Perkin's original feat that Kekulé and his structural formulas supplied organic chemists with a map of the territory, so to speak. Using that map, they could work out logical schemes of reaction, reasonable methods for altering a structural formula bit by bit in order to convert one molecule into another. It became possible to synthesize new organic chemicals not by accident, as in Perkin's triumph, but with deliberation.

Often the reactions worked out received the name of the discoverer. A method for adding two carbon atoms to a molecule, discovered by Perkin, is called the *Perkin reaction,* for instance; a method for breaking an atom ring containing a nitrogen atom, discovered by Perkin's teacher, is the *Hofmann degradation.*

Hofmann returned to Germany in 1864 and there threw himself into the new work of synthetic organic chemistry his young pupil had opened. He helped to found what, until World War I, remained almost a German monopoly of the field.

Natural dyes were duplicated in the laboratory. In 1867, Baeyer (of the "strain theory") began a program of research that eventually led to the synthesis of *indigo.* This achievement was, in the long run, to put the large indigo plantations in the Far East out of business. In 1868, a student of Baeyer's, Karl Graebe (1841–1927) synthesized alizarin, another important natural dye.

On such successes as these was founded the art and science of applied chemistry, which in the last few decades has so radically affected our lives and which goes on and on at an accelerating pace. A never-ending succession of new techniques for altering organic molecules has developed, and we must turn aside from the mainstream of chemical theory to examine some of the most important of them. Up to this point our history has lent itself to a straightforward narrative and a clear line of development, but in this and the next chapter we shall have to discuss a few individual advances among which very little connection is immediately apparent. Since these advances constitute the applications of chemistry to human needs, they are essential to our short history of the science though they may seem isolated from the main flow. In the last three chapters we return to the clear line of development of theory.

Drugs

Naturally occurring compounds of ever-increasing complexity were synthesized after Perkin. The synthetic substance, to be sure, could not compete with the natural product, in any economic sense, except in relatively rare cases, such as that of indigo. However, the synthesis usually served to establish the molecular structure, something that is always of vast theoretical (and sometimes practical) interest.

As examples, the German chemist Richard Willstätter (1872–1942) carefully worked out the structure of *chlorophyll,* the green, light-absorbing catalyst in plants which makes it possible to utilize the energy of sunlight in the production of carbohydrates from carbon dioxide.

Two German chemists, Heinrich Otto Wieland (1877–1957) and Adolf Windaus (1876–), worked out the structure of *steroids* and related compounds. (Among the steroids are a number of important hormones.) Another German chemist, Otto Wallach (1847–1931), painstakingly elucidated the structure of *terpenes,* important plant oils (of which menthol is a well-known example), while still another, Hans Fischer (1881–1945), established the structure of *heme,* the coloring matter of blood.

Vitamins, hormones, alkaloids, all have been probed in the twentieth century, and their molecular structures in many cases determined. For instance, in the 1930s, the Swiss chemist Paul Karrer (1889–) worked out the structure of the *carot-*

enoids, which are important plant pigments, and to which Vitamin A is closely related.

The English chemist Robert Robinson (1886–) tackled the alkaloids systematically. His greatest success was to work out the structure of *morphine* (except for one dubious atom) in 1925, and the structure of *strychnine* in 1946. Robinson's work on the latter was confirmed by the American chemist Robert Burns Woodward (1917–), who synthesized strychnine in 1954. Woodward began his triumphs in synthesis when he and his American colleague, William von Eggers Doering (1917–), synthesized *quinine* in 1944. It was the wild goose chase after this particular compound by Perkin which had had such tremendous results.

Woodward went on to synthesize more complicated organic molecules, including *cholesterol* (the most common of the steroids) in 1951, and *cortisone* (a steroid hormone) in the same year. In 1956, he synthesized *reserpine,* the first of the tranquillizers, and in 1960 he synthesized chlorophyll. In 1962, Woodward synthesized a complex compound related to the well-known antibiotic Achromycin.

Working in another direction, the Russian-American chemist Phoebus Aaron Theodor Levene (1869–1940) had deduced the structures of the *nucleotides,* which served as building blocks for the giant molecules of the nucleic acids. (The nucleic acids are now known to control the chemical workings of the body.) His conclusions were completely confirmed by the work of the Scottish chemist, Alexander Robertus Todd (1907–), who synthesized the various nucleotides, and related compounds as well, in the 1940s and early 1950s.

Some of these substances, notably the alkaloids, had medical uses and, therefore, come under the general heading of *drugs*. Quite early in the twentieth century, it was shown that complete synthetic products could have such uses, and could prove valuable drugs indeed.

The synthetic substance *arsphenamine* was used, in 1909, by the German bacteriologist Paul Ehrlich (1854–1915) as a therapeutic agent against syphilis. This application is taken as having founded the study of *chemotherapy,* the treatment of disease by the use of specific chemicals.

In 1908 a synthetic compound named *sulfanilamide* had been synthesized and added to the vast number of synthetics which were known but had no particular uses. In 1932, through the researches of the German chemist Gerhard Domagk (1895–), it was discovered that sulfanilamide and certain related compounds could be used to fight a variety of infectious diseases. But in this case natural products caught up to and surpassed the synthetics. The first example was *penicillin,* whose existence was discovered accidentally in 1928 by the Scottish bacteriologist Alexander Fleming (1881–1955). Fleming had left a culture of staphylococcus germs uncovered for some days and then found that it had become moldy. An unexpected circumstance caused him to look more closely. Around every speck of mold spore there showed a clear area where the bacterial culture had dissolved. He investigated matters as far as he could, suspecting the presence of an anti-bacterial drug, but the difficulties of isolating the material defeated him.

The need for drugs to combat infections in World War II resulted in another and more massive attack on the problem. Under the leadership of the Australian-English pathologist Howard Walter Florey (1898–) and the German-English biochemist

Ernst Boris Chain (1906–), penicillin was isolated and its structure determined. It was the first of the *antibiotics* ("against life," meaning microscopic life, of course). By 1945, a process of mold culture and concentration was producing half a ton of penicillin per month.

Chemists learned, in 1958, to stop the mold halfway, obtain the central core of the penicillin molecule, and then add to that core various organic groups that would not have occurred naturally. These synthetic analogs had, in some cases, infection-fighting properties superior to that of penicillin itself. Through the 1940s and 1950s, other antibiotics, such as streptomycin and the tetracyclines, were isolated from various molds and also brought into use.

The synthesis of complex organics could not be carried through without periodic analyses that would serve to identify the material obtained at various steps in the synthetic process. Usually, the material available for analysis was very small so that analyses were inaccurate at best and impossible at worst.

The Austrian chemist Fritz Pregl (1869–1930) successfully reduced the scale of equipment used in analysis. He obtained an exceedingly accurate balance, designed tiny pieces of glassware, and by 1913 had devised a thoroughgoing technique of *microanalysis*. Analyses of previously intractable small samples became accurate.

The classic methods of analysis usually involved measuring the volume of a substance consumed in a reaction (*volumetric analysis*), or the weight of a substance produced by a reaction (*gravimetric analysis*). As the twentieth century progressed, however, physical methods of analysis, involving light absorption, changes in electrical conductivity, and other even more sophisticated techniques, were introduced.

Proteins

The organic substances mentioned in the previous section are almost all made up of molecules that exist as single units, not easily broken up by mild chemical treatment, and made up of not more than perhaps fifty atoms. There exist, however, organic substances made up of molecules that are veritable giants, containing thousands, and even millions, of atoms. Such molecules are never unitary in nature but are always made up of rather small "building blocks."

It is easy to break down these giant molecules to the building blocks and study those. Levene did so in his study of nucleotides, for instance (see page 172). It was natural also to try to study the giant molecules intact, and by the mid-nineteenth century the first steps in this direction had been taken. The Scottish chemist Thomas Graham (1805–69) was the first, through his interest in *diffusion*–that is, the manner in which the molecules of two substances, brought into contact, will intermingle. He began by studying the rate of diffusion of gases through tiny holes or fine tubes. By 1831 he was able to show that the rate of diffusion of a gas was inversely proportional to the square root of its molecular weight (*Graham's law*).

Subsequently Graham passed to the study of the diffusion of dissolved substances. Solutions of substances like salt, sugar, or copper sulfate, he discovered, would find their way through a blocking sheet of parchment (presumably containing submicroscopic holes). On the other hand, dissolved materials such as gum arabic, glue, and gelatin would not. Clearly, the giant molecules of the latter group of substances would not fit through the holes in the parchment.

The materials that could pass through parchment (and happened to be easily obtained in crystalline form) Graham called *crystalloids*. Those that did not, like glue (in Greek, *kolla*), he called *colloids*. The study of giant molecules became an important part of the study of *colloid chemistry*, which Graham had thus opened up.[1]

Suppose pure water is on one side of a sheet of parchment and colloidal solution on the other. The water molecules can get into the colloidal chamber, but the colloidal molecules block the passage out. Water therefore moves into the colloidal portion of the system more readily than it moves out, and the imbalance sets up an *osmotic pressure*.

The German botanist Wilhelm Pfeffer (1845–1920) showed, in 1877, how one could measure this osmotic pressure and from measurements determine the molecular weight of the large molecules in colloidal solution. It was the first reasonably good method for estimating the size of such molecules.

An even better method was devised by a Swedish chemist, Theodor Svedberg (1884–). He developed the *ultracentrifuge* in 1923. This device spun colloidal solutions, forcing the giant molecules outward under huge centrifugal effects. From the rate at which the giant molecules moved outward, molecular weight could be determined.

Svedberg's assistant, Arne Wilhelm Kaurin Tiselius (1902–), another Swede, devised improved methods, in 1907, for separating giant molecules on

[1] In 1833, Graham had studied the various forms of phosphoric acid and showed that in some more than one hydrogen atom could be replaced by a metal. This introduced chemists to the existence of *polybasic acids*.

the basis of distributions of electric charge over the molecular surface. This technique, *electrophoresis,* was of particular importance in separating and purifying proteins.

Although physical methods were thus producing evidence concerning the over-all structure of giant molecules, chemists yearned to understand the chemical details of that structure. Their interest centered particularly on the proteins.

Whereas giant molecules such as starch and the cellulose of wood are built up of a single building block, endlessly repeated, the protein molecule is built up of some twenty different, but closely related, building blocks–the various amino acids (see page 97). It is for this reason that protein molecules are so versatile and offer so satisfactory a basis for the subtlety and variety of life. It also makes the protein molecule that much harder to characterize.

Emil Fischer, who had earlier determined the detailed structure of the sugar molecules (see page 123), grew interested in the protein molecule at the turn of the century. He demonstrated that the amine portion of one amino acid was bound to the acid portion of another to form a *peptide link.* He proved his case in 1907 by actually linking amino acids together in this fashion (eighteen of them altogether) and showing that the resulting compound possessed certain properties characteristic of proteins.

Determination of the order of the amino acids making up an actual *polypeptide chain* in a protein molecule as it occurs in nature, however, had to await the passage of another half-century, and the discovery of a new technique.

This technique began with the Russian botanist Mikhail Semenovich Tsvett (1872–1919). He let a solution of a mixture of very similar colored plant pigments trickle down a tube of powdered aluminum oxide. The different substances in the mixture held to the surface of the powder particles with different degrees of strength. As the mixture was washed downward, the individual components separated to form bands of color. Tsvett reported this effect in 1906 and called the technique *chromatography* ("color-writing").

This obscure Russian paper was ignored at first, but, in the 1920s, Willstätter (see page 171) and a student, the Austrian-German chemist Richard Kuhn (1900–), reintroduced the technique. It was refined, in 1944, by the English chemists Archer John Porter Martin (1910–) and Richard Laurence Millington Synge (1914–). They used absorbent filter paper rather than a column of powder. The mixture crept along the filter paper and separated; and this technique is called *paper chromatography*.

In the late 1940s and early 1950s, a number of proteins were broken down into their constituent amino acids. The amino acid mixtures were then separated and analyzed in detail by paper chromatography. In this way the total number of each amino acid present in the protein molecule was worked out, but not the exact order each held in the polypeptide chain. The English chemist Frederick Sanger (1918–) tackled insulin, a protein hormone made up of some fifty amino acids distributed among two interconnected polypeptide chains. He broke the molecule into smaller chains, and worked on each separately by paper chromatography. It took eight years of concentrated "jigsaw puzzle" work, but by 1953 the exact order of amino acids in the insulin molecule was worked out. The same methods have been used since 1953 to work out the detailed structure of even larger protein molecules.

The next step was to confirm such work by actually synthesizing a given protein molecule, amino acid by amino acid. In 1954, the American chemist Vincent du Vigneaud (1901–) made a beginning by synthesizing *oxytocin,* a small protein molecule made up of only eight amino acids. More complicated feats were quickly accomplished, however, and chains of dozens of amino acids were synthesized. By 1963 the amino acid chains of insulin itself had been built up in the laboratory.

Nevertheless, even the order of amino acids did not represent, in itself, all the useful knowledge concerning the molecular structure of proteins. When proteins are gently heated, they often lose, permanently, the properties of their natural state; they are *denatured.* The conditions that bring about denaturation are usually far too gentle to break up the polypeptide chain. The chain must therefore be bound into some definite structure by weak "secondary bonds." These secondary bonds usually involve a hydrogen atom lying between a nitrogen and oxygen atom. Such a *hydrogen bond* is only one-twentieth as strong as an ordinary valence bond.

In the early 1950s, the American chemist Linus Pauling (1901–) suggested that the polypeptide chain was coiled into a helical shape (like a "spiral staircase"), which was held in place by hydrogen bonds. This concept proved particularly useful in connection with the relatively simple *fibrous proteins* that make up skin and connective tissue.

Even the more intricately structured *globular proteins,* however, proved to be helical to a certain extent. The Austrian-British chemist Max Ferdinand Perutz (1914–) and the English chemist John Cowdery Kendrew (1917–) showed this when they determined the detailed structure of hemoglobin and myoglobin (the oxygen-gathering proteins of blood and muscle, respectively). In this analysis they made use of *x-ray diffraction,* a technique whereby a beam of x-rays passing through crystals is scattered by the atoms of which those crystals are composed. Scattering in a given direction and through a given angle is most effectively brought about when the atoms are arranged in a regular pattern. From the details of the scattering it is possible to work backward to the positions of the atoms within the molecule. For complicated arrangements such as those within sizable protein molecules the task is terribly tedious, but by 1960 the last detail of the myoglobin molecule (made up of twelve thousand atoms) had fallen into place.

Pauling had suggested also that his helical model might be made to fit the nucleic acids. The New Zealand-British physicist Maurice Hugh Frederick Wilkins (1916–) had, in the early 1950s, subjected nucleic acids to x-ray diffraction, and this work served to test Pauling's suggestion. The English physicist Francis Harry Compton Crick (1916–) and the American chemist James Dewey Watson (1928–) found an additional complication was required to suit the diffraction results. Each nucleic acid molecule had to be a double helix, two chains wound about a common axis. This Watson-Crick model, first advanced in 1953, proved an important breakthrough in the understanding of genetics.[2]

Explosives

Nor did the giant molecules escape the modifying hand of the chemist. The first case came about through an accidental discovery by the German-

[2] For further details on this subject, the interested reader is referred to my book *The Genetic Code* (Orion Press, 1963).

Swiss chemist Christian Friedrich Schönbein (1799–1868), who had already made his mark by discovering *ozone,* a form of oxygen.

In an experiment at his home, in 1845, he spilled a mixture of nitric and sulfuric acid and used his wife's cotton apron to mop it up. He hung the apron over the stove to dry, but once dry it went poof! and was gone. He had converted the cellulose of the apron into *nitrocellulose*. The nitro groups (added from the nitric acid) served as an internal source of oxygen, and when heated the cellulose was completely oxidized, all at once.

Schönbein recognized the possibilities of the compound. Ordinary black gunpowder exploded into thick smoke, blackening the gunners, fouling the cannon and small arms, and obscuring the battlefield. Nitrocellulose was a possible "smokeless powder," and from its potential as a propellant for artillery shells, it received the name *guncotton.*

Attempts to manufacture guncotton for military use failed at first, because the factories had a tendency to blow up. It was not till 1891 that Dewar (see page 166) and the English chemist Frederick Augustus Abel (1827–1902) managed to compound a safe mixture that included guncotton. Because the mixture could be pressed into long cords, it was called *cordite.* Thanks to cordite and its successors, soldiers of the twentieth century have enjoyed a clear field of view while slaughtering the enemy and being slaughtered.

One of the components of cordite is *nitroglycerine,* which had been discovered in 1847 by the Italian chemist Ascanio Sobrero (1812–88). It was a shattering explosive, also too touchy for war. Its use in peacetime to blast roads through mountains and to move tons of earth for a variety of purposes was also dangerous. Careless use heightened the death rate.

The family of Alfred Bernhard Nobel (1833–96), a Swedish inventor, manufactured nitroglycerine. When an explosion killed Nobel's brother, he bent his efforts to taming the explosive. In 1866, he found that an absorbent earth called "kieselguhr" could sponge up considerable quantities of nitroglycerine. The dampened kieselguhr could be molded into sticks which were perfectly safe to handle, but retained the shattering power of nitroglycerine itself. This safe explosive Nobel called *dynamite*. Being a humanitarian, he speculated with satisfaction that it would make war so horrible as to enforce peace. His motive was good but his assessment of human intelligence erred on the side of optimism.

The invention of new and better explosives toward the end of the nineteenth century was chemistry's first important contribution to warfare since the invention of gunpowder, over five centuries earlier, but the development of poison gases in World War I made it quite plain that mankind, in future wars, was going to pervert science to the work of destruction. The invention of the airplane and, eventually, of nuclear bombs (see page 252) made the lesson even plainer. Science, which up to the end of the nineteenth century had seemed an instrument for creating Utopia on earth, came to wear a mask of horrid doom to many men.

Polymers

There were many other directions, however, in which the peaceful uses of giant molecules predominated. Fully nitrated cellulose was an explosive to be sure, but partially nitrated cellulose (*pyroxylin*) was safer to handle, and important uses were developed for it.

The American inventor John Wesley Hyatt (1837–1920), in an attempt to win a prize offered for an ivory substitute for billiard balls, began with pyroxylin. He dissolved it in a mixture of alcohol and ether, then added camphor to make it softer and more malleable. By 1869 he had formed what he called *celluloid,* and won the prize. Celluloid was the first synthetic *plastic*—a material, that is, that can be molded into shape.

But if pyroxylin could be packed into spheres, it could also be pulled into fibers and films. The French chemist Louis Marie Hilaire Bernigaud, Count of Chardonnet (1839–1924), produced fibers by forcing solutions of pyroxylin through tiny holes. The squirting solvent evaporated almost at once, leaving a thread behind. These threads could be woven into material that had the glossiness of silk. In 1884, Chardonnet patented his *rayon* (so called since it was so shiny it seemed to give forth rays of light).

Plastic in film form came into its own, thanks to the interest of an American inventor, George Eastman (1854–1932), in photography. He learned to mix his emulsion of silver compounds with gelatin in order to make it dry. This mixture kept and did not have to be prepared on the spot. In 1884, he replaced the glass plate with celluloid film, which made matters so simple that photography, till then the province of the specialist, could become anyone's hobby.

Celluloid, while not explosive, was still too easily combustible, and represented a fire hazard. Eastman therefore experimented with less inflammable materials. When acetate groups rather than nitro groups were added to cellulose, the product was still plastic but was no longer dangerously inflammable. In 1924, cellulose acetate film was introduced, at a time when the developing motion picture industry particularly needed something to reduce the fire hazard.

Nor were chemists dependent upon only those giant molecules that already existed in nature. The Belgian-American chemist Leo Hendrik Baekeland (1863–1944) was searching for a shellac substitute. For the purpose, he wanted a solution of some gummy, tarlike substance that resulted from the addition of small molecular units into a giant molecule. The small molecule is a *monomer* ("one part"), and the final product a *polymer* ("many parts").

The manner in which monomers join to form giant molecules, it should be explained, is not mysterious. To take a simple case, consider two molecules of ethylene (C_2H_4). The structural formulas are

$$
\begin{array}{ccccc}
H & & & & H \\
 & \diagdown & & \diagup & \\
 & & C{=}C & & \\
 & \diagup & & \diagdown & \\
H & & & & H
\end{array}
\qquad\qquad
\begin{array}{ccccc}
H & & & & H \\
 & \diagdown & & \diagup & \\
 & & C{=}C & & \\
 & \diagup & & \diagdown & \\
H & & & & H
\end{array}
$$

If we imagine a hydrogen atom shifted from one to the other, and one double bond changing to a single bond, so that a new bond can be used to connect the two molecules, we end with a four-carbon substance:

$$
\begin{array}{cccccccc}
 & H & & H & & H & & H \\
 & | & & | & & | & \diagup & \\
H & -C & - & C & - & C & {=}C & \\
 & | & & | & & & \diagdown & \\
 & H & & H & & & & H
\end{array}
$$

Such a four-carbon molecule still has a double bond. It can therefore combine with yet another ethylene molecule, by way of the shift of a hydrogen atom and the opening of its double bond, to form a six-carbon molecule with one double bond. The same process will next lead to an eight-carbon molecule, then to a ten-carbon molecule and, indeed, to a molecule of almost any desired length.[3]

Baekeland began with phenol and formaldehyde as the monomer units and produced a polymer for which he could not find a solvent. It occurred to him that a polymer so hard and solvent-resistant might be useful for those very reasons. It could be molded as it formed and then allowed to set into a hard, water-resistant, solvent-resistant, non-conductor of electricity, which yet could be machined easily. In 1909 he announced the existence of what he called *Bakelite,* the first and still, in some ways, one of the most useful of the completely synthetic plastics.

Completely synthetic fibers were also to take their place in the world. The leader, here, was the American chemist Wallace Hume Carothers (1896–1937). He, together with a Belgian-American chemist, Julius Arthur Nieuwland (1878–1936), had investigated polymers related to, and having some of the elastic properties of, rubber.[4] The result, in

[3] The extent to which this *polymerization* proceeds depends on the length of time the monomers are allowed to react, the temperature and pressure under which they react, the presence or absence of other substances which may hasten or slow the reaction, and so on. The modern chemist, taking all this into account can virtually design his own final product.

[4] Rubber is a natural polymer produced by certain tropical plants. In its natural state, it is too sticky in warm weather, too hard in cold weather to be completely useful. The American inventor Charles Goodyear (1800–60) discovered, partly by accident, that rubber, heated with sulfur,

1932, was *Neoprene,* one of the "synthetic rubbers" or, as they are now called, *elastomers.*

Carothers went on to work with other polymers. Allowing the molecules of certain diamines and dicarboxylic acids to polymerize, he produced fibers made up of long molecules that contained atom combinations similar to the peptide links (see page 177) in silk protein. These synthetic fibers, after stretching, are what we now call *nylon.* It was developed just before Carothers' too-early death, but World War II intervened, and it was not until after that conflict that nylon came to replace silk in almost all its uses, particularly in hosiery.

At first, synthetic polymers were built up through the processes of trial and error, for little was known about the structure of giant molecules or the details of the required reactions. An early leader in the studies of polymer structure, who removed many of the uncertainties, was the German chemist Hermann Staudinger (1881–). Some of the weaknesses of synthetic polymers came to be understood through his work. It was possible, for instance, for monomers to add to each other in random fashion so that atomic groups on the individual units might point in one direction here in the chain and in another direction there. This randomness would tend to weaken the final product by not allowing the molecular chains to pack together well. Chains might even branch, which would make matters still worse.

The German chemist Karl Ziegler (1898–) discovered, in 1953, that he could use a resin (a

---

remained dry and pliant over a wide range of temperatures. He patented his *vulcanized rubber* in 1844. Rubber truly came into its own in the twentieth century, with the development of the automobile and the need for tires in huge quantities.

natural plant polymer), to which atoms of aluminum, titanium, or lithium might be attached, as catalysts. These catalysts would bring about a more orderly combination of monomers, and branching was eliminated.

Through similar work by the Italian chemist Giulio Natto (1903–), combinations were so ordered that atomic groupings were arranged in orderly fashion down the polymer chain. In short, the art of polymerization reached the point where plastics, films, and fibers could be produced virtually to order, fulfilling properties specified in advance.

One great source of the basic organic substances needed to produce the new synthetics in the huge quantities required was *petroleum.* This fluid had been known since ancient times, but use of it in quantity had to await development of a technique for tapping the vast subterranean pools. Edwin Laurentine Drake (1819–80), an American inventor, was the first to drill for oil, in 1859. In the century since Drake, petroleum, as everyone knows, has become the prime ingredient of our society–the principal source of organics, of heat for our homes, and of power for moving objects, from airplanes and automobiles down to scooters and lawn mowers.

Coal, though we tend to forget it in this age of the internal combustion engine, is an even more common source of organic materials. The Russian chemist Vladimir Nikolaevich Ipatieff (1867–1952), around the turn of the century, began researches into the reactions of the complex hydrocarbons in oil and in coal tar at high temperatures. A German chemist, Friedrich Karl Rudolf Bergius (1884–1949), used Ipatieff's findings to devise, in 1912, practical methods for treating coal and heavy oil with hydrogen in order to make gasoline.

Still, the world's total supply of *fossil fuels* (coal

plus oil) is limited and is, in many ways, irreplaceable. According to all current surveys, total depletion of the supply is in view for a day of reckoning that is not unbelievably far ahead. While the twentieth century is safe to its end, there is reason for concern over the twenty-first century, particularly in view of mankind's rapidly expanding numbers and consequently increased demands.

CHAPTER 11

INORGANIC CHEMISTRY

The New Metallurgy

If the nineteenth century, particularly the latter half, seems pre-eminently the era of organic chemistry, inorganic chemistry was nevertheless far from remaining at a standstill.

Photography already has been mentioned (see page 184) as an important nineteenth-century application of inorganic chemistry, but in its importance to the economy or the well-being of society it must be regarded, of course, as a minor contribution. Another of those small contributions, usually taken for granted but with social significance for all that, was an advance in firemaking technique. Through all history mankind had been making fires either by applying friction to objects such as wood, which had to be heated to high temperatures before it would catch fire, or by striking sparks that lasted but a moment, as with flint-and-steel. But in time men began to experiment with chemicals which would burst into flame at low temperatures that could be reached with brief friction. In 1827, the English inventor John Walker (c. 1781–1859) devised the first practical phosphorus match. It has been much improved in the century and a half since, but the principle remains.

Photography and the phosphorus match are only

two examples of many practical advances in inorganic chemistry that would deserve more than mere mention in a full-dress, detailed history of the science, but in this short work we must concentrate on the larger affairs. The most dramatic progress in the applied chemistry of the nineteenth century was made in metals, of which steel was, and continues to be, the most important to our economy. Petroleum feeds and fuels our society, but steel forms its supporting skeleton.

Although steelworking, as we have seen, was common even three thousand years ago, it was not until the mid-nineteenth century that a technique was devised for producing it cheaply enough and in the huge quantities required for the framework of modern society. The great name here is Henry Bessemer (1813–98).

Bessemer, an English metallurgist, was attempting to devise an artillery projectile that would spin in flight and move in an accurately predictable path. For this he needed a cannon that was rifled–that is, had spiral grooves cut in the bore wall from breach to muzzle. The barrel had to be made of particularly strong steel, however, to withstand the great pressures required to force the emerging projectiles against the spiral grooves and thus into a rapid spin. Ordinary unrifled cannon, used at that time, could be made of weaker material, and steel was quite expensive. Unless something was done, then, Bessemer's rifled cannon was quite impractical.

Iron, as produced, was *cast iron,* rich in carbon (from the coke or charcoal used to smelt the ore). Cast iron was exceedingly hard, but brittle. The carbon could be painstakingly removed to form *wrought iron,* which was tough, but relatively soft. A proper amount of carbon was then re-introduced, just enough to form steel, which was both tough and hard.

Bessemer looked for a method that would produce iron plus just enough carbon to form steel without going through the expensive wrought iron stage. To remove the excess carbon in cast iron he sent a blast of air through the molten metal. This air did not cool and solidify the metal. On the contrary, the heat of combination of carbon and oxygen actually raised the temperature of the melt. By stopping the air blast at the right time, Bessemer could obtain steel. (See Figure 19.)

In 1856, he announced his *blast furnace*. At first, attempts to duplicate his work failed because his method required phosphorus-free ore to begin with. Once this was realized, things went smoothly, steel became cheap, and the Iron Age (see page 7) finally gave way to the Steel Age. (Subsequently, techniques superior to Bessemer's were introduced into steel production.) It is the strength of steel that has made modern skyscrapers and suspension bridges possible; it was steel that armored battleships and provided monster artillery pieces, and steel on which trains ran.

Nor did steelmaking stop at the combination of carbon and iron. The English metallurgist Robert Abbot Hadfield (1858–1940) tested the properties of steel to which quantities of other metals were added. Adding manganese seemed to make steel brittle, but Hadfield added more than previous metallurgists had attempted. By the time the steel was 12 per cent manganese it was no longer brittle. When heated to 1000° C. and then quenched in water, it became much harder than ordinary steel. Hadfield patented his manganese steel in 1882, and that event marks the beginning of the triumph of *alloy steel.*

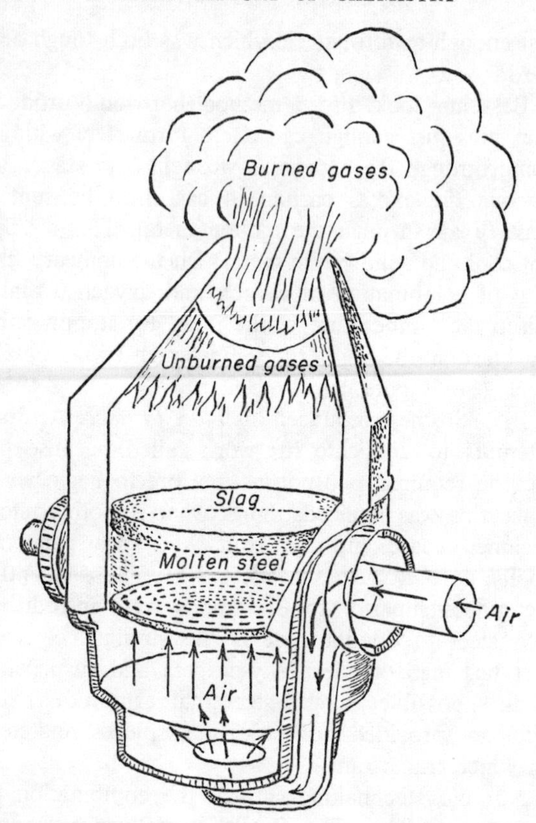

FIG. 19. Bessemer converter revolutionized the production of steel.

Other metals were successfully added to steel, chromium, molybdenum, vanadium, tungsten, niobium, forming varieties of alloy steel suitable for particular purposes. By 1919 a non-rusting *stainless steel,* containing chromium and nickel, had been patented by the American inventor Elwood Haynes (1857–1925). In 1916, Japanese metallurgist Kotaro Honda (1870–1954) found that adding cobalt to tungsten steel produced an alloy capable of forming a more powerful magnet than ordinary steel. This discovery opened the way to still stronger magnetic alloys.

Altogether new metals came into use, too. *Aluminum,* for instance, is more common in the earth's soil than iron is; indeed, it is the most common of all metals. However, it remains firmly combined in compounds. Whereas iron has been known and prepared from its ores since prehistoric times, aluminum was not even recognized as a metal until Wöhler (see page 95) isolated an impure sample in 1827.

Not until 1855 did a French chemist, Henri Etienne Sainte-Claire Deville (1818–81), work out an adequate method for preparing reasonably pure aluminum in moderate quantities. Even then, it was far more expensive than steel, so that it was used for ostentation, as, for instance, for the rattle of Napoleon III's infant son, or the cap at the top of the Washington Monument.

In 1886, however, a young American student of chemistry, Charles Martin Hall (1863–1914), hearing his teacher say that anyone discovering a cheap way of making aluminum would grow rich and famous, determined to tackle the problem. Working in his home laboratory, he discovered that aluminum oxide could be made to dissolve in a molten mineral called cryolite. Once the oxide was in solution, electrolysis would produce aluminum itself. In the same year, the French metallurgist Paul Louis Toussaint Héroult (1863–1914) devised essentially the same method for producing the metal. The Hall-Héroult method made aluminum cheap and fit for even the most plebeian use–down to the kitchen saucepan.

Aluminum's greatest value lies in its lightness

(one-third the weight of steel). This quality makes it of particular use to the aircraft industry, which also devours quantities of *magnesium,* an even lighter metal. Practical methods were devised in the 1930s for extracting magnesium metals from the salts dissolved in the ocean, giving us now a virtually inexhaustible source of the metal. (Bromine and iodine–to say nothing of salt itself–are now profitably obtained from the ocean. A problem of growing importance for the future is that of extracting fresh water itself from the ocean.)

Metals such as *titanium* show great promise, too. Titanium is a common metal, highly resistant to acids, intermediate in lightness between aluminum and steel, and, properly prepared, the strongest of the metals, weight for weight. *Zirconium* is similar, but is less common and is heavier.

Titanium's outlook for the future is particularly bright in connection with the supersonic planes being designed and built. Planes moving through even the thin upper atmosphere at speeds that are multiples of the speed of sound undergo considerable frictional resistance from the air. Their outer skin must withstand high temperatures, and here titanium is particularly suitable, for it retains its strength at high temperature better than other metals do.

Nitrogen and Fluorine

Nitrogen surrounds us in the atmosphere, but there it is present in elementary form. To most organisms it is useful only in compound form. As it happens, nitrogen is almost inert and reacts to form compounds only with difficulty. Despite the omnipresence of air, then, soil is often short of nitrates (the most common type of nitrogen compound), and they must be supplied in the form of animal wastes or chemical fertilizers. Nitrates are also ingredients of gunpowder, and are used, indirectly, in the formation of the newer explosives, such as nitrocellulose and nitroglycerine.

The earth's supply of nitrates is kept in being through the activity of thunderstorms. The nitrogen and oxygen of the air combine in the vicinity of lightning bolts to form compounds. These compounds dissolve in the raindrops and are brought to earth. In addition, certain types of bacteria utilize elementary nitrogen from the air to produce nitrogen compounds. But as man's requirement for nitrates, both for fertilizers and for explosives, grew, it became difficult to rely on natural sources alone. The German chemist Fritz Haber (1868–1934) investigated methods for combining atmospheric nitrogen with hydrogen to form ammonia. The ammonia could then be converted easily into nitrates. By 1908 Haber had managed to perform the task by placing nitrogen and hydrogen under high pressure and using iron as a catalyst.

With the coming of World War I, and the blockade of Germany by the British fleet, Germany could no longer obtain natural nitrate from the Chilean desert (the best natural source). The German chemist Karl Bosch (1874–1940) had, however, changed the Haber process from a laboratory demonstration into an industrial operation. By the middle of the war he was producing all the nitrogen compounds Germany needed.

Just the reverse was the case of fluorine, so active that it existed only in compounds and defied the efforts of chemists to set it free. Since the time of Lavoisier, however, chemists were certain that the element existed; so certain were they, in fact, that Newlands and Mendeléev included it in their periodic tables (see pages 130, 135), though no man had ever seen it. To be sure, electrolysis would break fluorine away from its various compound molecules. However, as soon as the gas was in elemental form it would react with whatever was closest and become part of a compound again. (Fluorine is the most active of all chemical elements.)

Many chemists tackled the problem in the nineteenth century, from Davy onward. It was left to the French chemist Ferdinand Frédéric Henri Moissan (1852–1907) to succeed. Moissan decided that since platinum was one of the few substances that could resist fluorine, there was nothing to do but prepare all his equipment of platinum, regardless of expense. What's more, he chilled everything to −50° C. to dull fluorine's fierce activity. In 1886, he passed an electric current through a solution of potassium fluoride in hydrofluoric acid in his all-platinum equipment and achieved his goal. The pale-yellow gas, fluorine, was finally isolated.

Though this was a great feat, Moissan became even more famous for another achievement that was not really an achievement at all. Charcoal and diamond are both forms of carbon and differ only in that the carbon atoms in diamond are packed with great compactness. It follows that if great pressure is placed on charcoal, the atoms might rearrange more compactly to form diamond. Moissan tried to accomplish this by dissolving charcoal in molten iron and letting the carbon crystallize out as the iron cooled.

By 1893, it seemed to him he had succeeded. He produced several tiny, impure diamonds together with a sliver of good diamond, over half a millimeter in length. It is possible, however, that Moissan was the victim of a hoax and that some assistant had seeded the iron. We now know, from theoretical considerations, that under the conditions Moissan used, diamond could not have formed.

An American inventor, Edward Goodrich Acheson (1856–1931), also attempted the formation of diamond from more ordinary forms of carbon. He failed, but in the process, while heating carbon intensely in the presence of clay, he obtained an extremely hard substance which he named *carborundum*. It proved to be silicon carbide (a compound of silicon and carbon), and formed an excellent abrasive.

To form diamonds, pressures higher than any available in the nineteenth century had to be used, together with high temperatures which would make it possible for atoms to alter their positions with reasonable ease. The American physicist Percy William Bridgman (1882–1961) spent half a century, beginning in 1905, devising equipment that would yield higher and higher pressures. Various elements and compounds took up new forms, ones in which atoms and molecules packed into unusually compact arrangements. Varieties of ice, for instance, considerably denser than water and with a melting point higher than the boiling point of water at ordinary pressures, were produced.[1] In 1955, using Bridgman's techniques, truly synthetic diamonds were finally formed.

Inorganic-Organic Borderland

With the twentieth century a vast region on the borderland between organic and inorganic chemistry began to open up.

The English chemist Frederick Stanley Kipping

[1] Such high-pressure forms revert to ordinary forms as soon as the pressure is relieved, usually. Diamond is an exception.

(1863–1949) began, in 1899, research on organic compounds containing the element silicon which, next to oxygen, is the most common element in the earth's rocky crust. Over a period of forty years he managed to synthesize a large number of organic compounds containing one or more of these atoms so characteristic of the inorganic world. Indeed, it was possible to obtain indefinitely long chains made up of silicon and oxygen atoms in alternation.

This work might be viewed as purely inorganic, but each silicon atom has a valence of four, of which only two are used in combination with oxygen. The other two, therefore, can be bound to any of a variety of organic groupings. In World War II and afterward, such inorganic/organic *silicones* gained importance as greases, hydraulic fluids, synthetic rubbers, water repellents, and so on.

Ordinary organic compounds are composed of carbon atoms to which other atoms are attached. In general, the majority of the "other atoms" are hydrogens, so that organic compounds may be spoken of as the hydrocarbons and their derivatives. The fluorine atom, however, is almost as small as the hydrogen atom and will fit anywhere the hydrogen atom will. One would expect that there should exist a whole family of *fluorocarbons* and their derivatives.

An early experimenter with fluoro-organic compounds was the American chemist Thomas Midgley, Jr. (1889–1944). In 1930 he prepared *freon,* with a molecule consisting of a carbon atom to which two chlorine atoms and two fluorine atoms are attached. It is easily liquefied so that it can be used as a refrigerant, in place of those other easily liquefied gases ammonia and sulfur dioxide. Unlike them, freon is odorless and non-toxic and completely non-flammable, too. It is now used almost universally in home refrigerators and air-conditioners.

During World War II, fluorine and fluorine compounds were used in connection with the work on uranium and the atomic bomb (see page 251). Greases were needed that would not be attacked by fluorine and, for the purpose, fluorocarbons were used, since these already have undergone (so to speak) maximum attack by fluorine.

Fluorine forms a very tight bond with carbon, and fluorocarbon chains are more stable and more inert than hydrocarbon chains. Fluorocarbon polymers are waxy, water-repellent, solvent-repellent, electrically insulating substances. A fluorocarbon plastic (*Teflon*) has come into use, in the 1960s, as a film to cover frying pans, which then no longer require fat for frying.

Inorganic complexity does not require the carbon atom at all in some cases. The German chemist Alfred Stock (1876–1946) began the study of boron hydrides (compounds of boron and hydrogen) in 1909. He found that fairly complicated compounds could be built up, compounds analogous, in some ways, to the hydrocarbons.

Since World War II, boron hydrides have gained an unexpected use as rocket fuel additives designed to increase the push that forces rockets into the upper atmosphere and outer space. Further, the boron hydrides proved of theoretical interest, because the ordinary formulas of the type first devised by Kekulé (see page 100) were inadequate to explain their structure.

But all these accomplishments, however ingeniously and painstakingly arrived at, however essential to the modern way of life, were extraneous to the most serious business of twentieth-century chemistry. The pure scientist was probing beneath the surface of the atom, and as we look at what he found there, we return, for the remainder of this book, to the main line of development in our history.

CHAPTER 12

ELECTRONS

Cathode Rays

When Leucippus and his disciple Democritus first advanced the notion of atoms (see page 13), they pictured the atom as the ultimate, indivisible particle. Dalton, over two thousand years later, retained that view (see page 73). It seemed necessary to suppose the atom to have no internal structure by definition. If the atom could be divided into still smaller entities, then would not those smaller entities be the true atoms?

Throughout the nineteenth century this view of the atom as a featureless, structureless, indivisible particle persisted. When the view broke down, it was through a line of experimentation that was not chemical in nature at all. It came about, instead, through studies of the electric current.

If a concentration of positive electric charge exists in one place and a concentration of negative electric charge exists in another, an *electric potential* is set up between the two. Under the driving force of this electric potential a current of electricity flows from one point of concentration to the other, this current tending to equalize the concentration.

The current flows through some materials more easily than others. The various metals are *conductors,* for instance, and even a small electric potential suffices to drive a current through them. Substances such as glass, mica, and sulfur are *non-conductors* or *insulators,* and it requires enormous electric potentials to drive even small currents through them.

Nevertheless, given enough electric potential, a current could be driven through any material, solid, liquid, or gaseous. Some liquids (a salt solution, for instance) conduct electric currents quite easily, in fact, as the first experimenters learned early in the game. Then, too, a lightning bolt represents an electric current momentarily being carried through miles of air.

It seemed reasonable to the nineteenth-century experimenters to carry the matter one step further and to make attempts to drive an electric current across a vacuum. To obtain meaningful results, however, one had to have a vacuum sufficiently good to allow the current to cross (if it were going to) without significant interference from matter.

Faraday's attempts to drive electricity through a vacuum failed for lack of a good enough vacuum. In 1855, however, a German glassblower, Heinrich Geissler (1814–79), devised a method for producing vacuums better than any that had previously been obtained. He prepared glass vessels, so evacuated. A friend of his, the German physicist Julius Plücker (1801–68), used such *Geissler tubes* for electrical experimentation.

Plücker had two electrodes sealed in such tubes, set up an electric potential between them, and succeeded in driving a current across. The current produced glowing effects within the tube, and those effects changed according to just how good the vacuum was. If the vacuum was very good the glow would fade out, but the glass of the tube around the anode gave off a green light.

The English physicist William Crookes (1832–

1919) had devised, by 1875, a still better evacuated tube (a *Crookes tube*), in which the electric current through a vacuum could more easily be studied. It seemed quite clear that the electric current started at the cathode and traveled to the anode, where it struck the neighboring glass and created the glow of light. Crookes demonstrated this by placing a piece of metal in the tube and showing that it cast a shadow on the glass on the side opposite the cathode.[1]

At the time, however, physicists did not know what an electric current might be and they could not easily tell just what it was that was moving from the cathode to the anode. Whatever it was, it traveled in straight lines (for it cast sharp shadows), so without committing oneself to any decision as to its nature, one could refer to it as a "radiation." Indeed, in 1876, the German physicist Eugen Goldstein (1850–1930) named the flow *cathode rays.*

It seemed natural to suspect that the cathode rays might be a form of light, and be made up of waves. Waves traveled in straight lines, like light, and, like light, seemed unaffected by gravity. On the other hand, it might equally well be inferred that the cathode rays consisted of speeding particles, which, because they were so light or moved so quickly (or both), were affected by gravity not at all or only by indetectable amounts. For some decades the matter was one of considerable controversy, with the German physicists strongly for waves and the English physicists strongly for particles.

One way to decide between the alternatives would

[1] The electrical experimenters of the eighteenth and nineteenth centuries, beginning with Benjamin Franklin, had assumed that the current flowed from the concentration arbitrarily named positive to that named negative (see page 78). Crookes had now shown that, in actual fact, the assumption was wrong and that the flow was from negative to positive.

be to find out whether the cathode rays were deflected to one side by the action of a magnet. Particles might themselves be magnets, or might carry an electric charge, and in either case, they would be far more easily deflected by such a field than waves would.

Plücker himself had actually shown this deflection to exist, and Crookes had done so independently. There still remained a question, however. If the cathode rays consisted of charged particles, an electric field should deflect them, too, but at first that effect was not demonstrated.

In 1897, however, the English physicist Joseph John Thomson (1856–1940), working with very highly evacuated tubes, was finally able to show cathode ray deflection in an electric field. (See Figure 20.) That was the final link in the chain of evidence, and it had to be accepted that the cathode rays were streams of particles carrying a negative electric charge. The amount by which a cathode ray particle is deflected in a magnetic field of given strength is determined by its mass and by the size of its electric charge. Thomson was therefore able to measure the

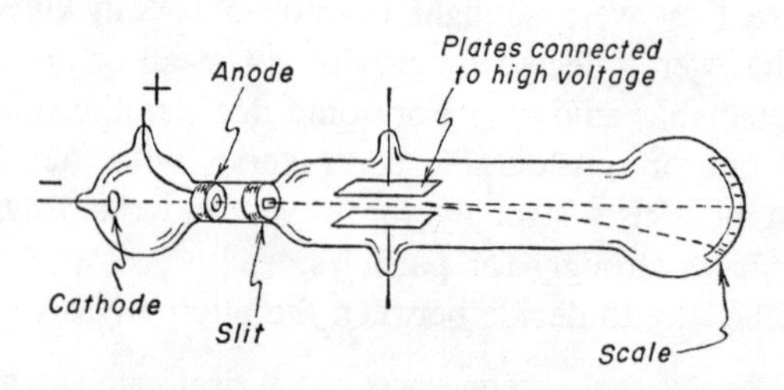

FIG. 20. Cathode ray tube enabled Thomson to measure deflection of electron beams in electric fields of known strength. Beam passed between the plates, whose field deflected electrons, shifting their striking points along the scale.

ratio of the mass to the charge, though he couldn't measure either separately.

The smallest mass known was that of the hydrogen atom, and if the cathode-ray particle was assumed to have that mass it would have to carry an electric charge hundreds of times greater than the smallest charge known (that on the hydrogen ion). If, on the other hand, the cathode-ray particle was assumed to have the minimum charge observed in ions, then its mass would have to be only a small fraction of that of the hydrogen atom. One of these alternatives was necessary, from Thomson's determination of the mass-charge ratio.

There were good reasons for preferring the latter alternative and assuming the cathode-ray particle to be much smaller than any atom. By 1911 this was proven definitely by the American physicist Robert Andrews Millikan (1868–1953), who succeeded in measuring, quite accurately, the minimum electric charge that could be carried by a particle.

If this charge were carried by the cathode-ray particle, it would have to be only 1/1837 as massive as a hydrogen atom. It was thus the first of the *sub-atomic particles* to be discovered.

Ever since the time of Faraday's laws of electrolysis (see page 90), it had seemed that electricity might be carried by particles. In 1891, the Irish physicist George Johnstone Stoney (1826–1911) had even suggested a name for the fundamental unit of electricity, whether particle or not. He suggested the name *electron.*

Now here, at last, in the form of the cathode-ray particle, was the "atom of electricity" about which men had speculated for over half a century. Those particles came to be called electrons, as Stoney had suggested, and J. J. Thomson is therefore considered to have discovered the electron.

The Photoelectric Effect

It remained to be determined whether there was any connection between the electron and the atom. The electron might be the particle of electricity and the atom might be the particle of matter; and both might be structureless, ultimate particles, completely independent of each other.

It seemed quite clear, however, that the independence could not be complete. Arrhenius, in the 1880s, had advanced his theory of ionic dissociation (see page 161). He had explained the behavior of ions by assuming them to be electrically charged atoms or groups of atoms. At the time this had seemed nonsense to most chemists, but it seemed nonsense no longer.

Suppose an electron attached itself to a chlorine atom. In that case, one would have a chlorine atom carrying a single negative charge, and this would be the *chloride ion.* If two electrons attached themselves to an atom-group made up of a sulfur atom and four oxygen atoms, the result would be a doubly-charged *sulfate ion,* and so on. In this way one could easily explain all negatively charged ions.

But how would one explain positively charged ions? The *sodium ion,* for instance, was a sodium atom carrying one positive charge. No positively charged particle quite analogous to the electron was then known, so one could not take the easy way out of supposing that atoms might attach themselves to such positively charged particles.

An alternative suggestion was that the positive charge might be created by withdrawing an electron or two from the atom, an electron or two that had been present as part of the atom itself!

This revolutionary possibility was made the more

plausible because of a phenomenon first observed in 1888 by the German physicist Heinrich Rudolf Hertz (1857–1894) during the course of experiments in which he discovered radio waves.

While sending an electric spark across an air gap from one electrode to another, Hertz found that when ultraviolet light shone on the cathode, the spark was more easily emitted. This, together with other electrical phenomena brought about by the shining of light upon metal, was eventually termed the *photoelectric effect.*

In 1902, the German physicist Philipp Eduard Anton Lenard (1862–1947) who, in earlier life, had been an assistant in Hertz's laboratory, showed that the photoelectric effect was brought about by the emission of electrons from metal.

A wide variety of metals was subject to photoelectric effects, and all these metals could emit electrons on the impact of light even when there was no electric current or electric charge in the vicinity. It seemed reasonable to suppose, then, that metal atoms (and, presumably, all atoms) contained electrons.

But atoms in their normal state did not carry an electric charge. If they contained negatively charged electrons, they must also contain a balancing positive charge. Lenard thought that atoms might consist of clouds of both negative and positive particles equal in all respects but charge. This possibility, however, seemed quite unlikely, for if it were so, why were not positively charged particles ever emitted by the atom? Why was it always, and only, the electron?

J. J. Thomson suggested, then, that the atom was a solid sphere of positively charged material with negatively charged electrons stuck into it, like raisins in poundcake. In the ordinary atom the negative charge of the electrons just neutralized the positive charge of the atom itself. Adding additional electrons gave the atom a net negative charge, while prying loose some of the original electrons gave it a net positive charge.

However, the notion of a solid, positively charged atom did not hold up. While positively charged particles exactly comparable to an electron remained unknown in the early decades of the twentieth century, other kinds of positively charged particles were discovered.

In 1886, Goldstein (who had given cathode rays their name) did some experimenting with a perforated cathode in an evacuated tube. When cathode rays were given off in one direction toward the anode, other rays found their way through the holes in the cathode and sped off in the opposite direction.

Since these other rays traveled in the direction opposite to the negatively charged cathode rays, it seemed that they must be composed of positively charged particles. This hypothesis was confirmed when the manner in which they were deflected in a magnetic field was studied. In 1907, J. J. Thomson named them *positive rays*.

The positive rays differed from electrons in more than charge. All electrons had the same mass, but the positive-rays particles came in different masses, depending on what gases were present (in traces) in the evacuated tube. Furthermore, whereas the electrons were only 1/1837th as massive as even the lightest atom, the positive ray particles were fully as massive as atoms. Even the lightest positive ray particle was as massive as the hydrogen atom.

The New Zealand-born physicist Ernest Rutherford (1871–1937) finally decided to accept the fact that the unit of positive charge was a particle quite different from the electron, which was the unit of negative charge. He suggested, in 1914, that the smallest positive ray particle, the one as massive as the hydrogen atom, be accepted as the fundamental unit of positive charge. He was confirmed in this view by his later experiments on nuclear reactions (see page 242) when he frequently found himself producing an identical particle as a hydrogen-nucleus. In 1920, Rutherford suggested that this fundamental positive particle be called the *proton.*

Radioactivity

Positively charged particles turned up, also, by way of a completely different line of experimentation.

A German physicist, Wilhelm Konrad Röntgen (1845–1923), was interested in the ability of cathode rays to cause certain chemicals to glow. In order to observe the faint light that was produced, he darkened the room and enclosed his evacuated tube in thin, black cardboard. In 1895 he was working with such a tube when a flash of light that did not come from the tube caught his eye. Quite a distance from the tube was a sheet of chemically coated paper, glowing away. It glowed only when the cathode rays were in action, not otherwise.

Röntgen concluded that when the cathode rays struck the anode some form of radiation was created which could pass through the glass of the tube and the surrounding cardboard and strike materials outside. In fact, if he took the chemically coated paper into the next room, it still glowed whenever the cathode rays were in action, so one had to conclude that the radiation was capable of penetrating walls. Röntgen called this penetrating radiation *x-rays,* and they have retained that name to the present. (It was eventually determined that x-rays were like light

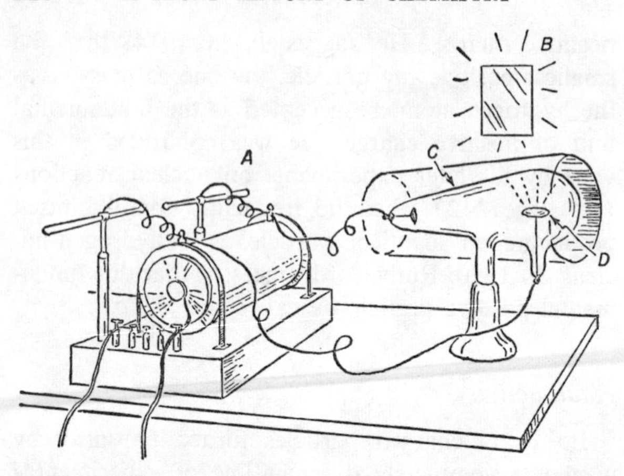

FIG. 21. X-ray apparatus used by Röntgen consisted of: (A) high-voltage induction coil; (B) paper painted with barium platinocyanide, which glowed when struck by rays; (C) the tube surrounded with a cylindrical black cardboard cover; (D) the cathode, which emitted electrons.

waves in nature, but much more energetic.) (See Figure 21.)

The world of physics grew very interested in x-rays at once, and among those who began experiments in connection with it was the French physicist Antoine Henri Becquerel (1852–1908). He was interested in the ability of some chemicals to glow with a characteristic light of their own (*fluorescence*) upon being exposed to sunlight. He wondered if the fluorescent glow contained x-rays.

In 1896, Becquerel wrapped photographic film in black paper and put it in sunlight, with a crystal of a uranium compound resting on it. The crystal was a fluorescent substance, and if the glow were simply ordinary light, it would not pass through the black paper or affect the photographic film. If x-rays were present, they would pass through the paper and fog the film. Sure enough, Becquerel found his film fogged. He discovered, however, that if the crystal was not exposed to the sun and was not fluorescing, it fogged the photographic film anyway. In short, the crystals were emitting penetrating radiation at all times!

Marie Sklodowska Curie (1867–1934), the first famous woman scientist, gave this phenomenon the name of *radioactivity*. She determined that it wasn't the whole uranium compound but the uranium atom specifically that was radioactive. Whether the atom was in the metallic elementary form, or combined in any compound whatever, it was radioactive. In 1898 she discovered that the heavy metal, thorium, was radioactive also. Mme. Curie, a Pole by birth, did her research with the help of her French husband, Pierre Curie, a physicist of note.

The radiation given off by uranium and thorium was found soon enough to be complex in nature. When a stream of such radiation was passed through a magnetic field, some was slightly deflected in one direction, some was strongly deflected in the opposite direction, and some was unaffected. Rutherford gave these three components of the radiation the names *alpha rays, beta rays,* and *gamma rays,* respectively, from the first three letters of the Greek alphabet.

Since the gamma rays were undeflected by the magnetic field, it was decided they were light-like radiation, like x-rays, in fact, but even more energetic. The beta rays were deflected in the direction and by the amount that cathode rays would have been deflected. Becquerel had decided that these rays were composed of speeding electrons. The individual electrons emitted by radioactive substances are therefore called *beta particles.* That left the nature of alpha rays still to be determined.

Experiments with alpha rays in magnetic fields showed deflection opposite to that of the beta rays. The alpha rays, therefore, had to be positively charged. They were only very slightly deflected, so they must be very massive; in fact, as it turned out, they were four times as massive as the particles Rutherford had named protons.

This ratio of weights seemed to indicate that alpha rays might consist of particles made up of four protons each. But if this were so, one of the particles ought to have a positive charge equal to that of four protons; however, as was discovered, its charge was equal to that of only two protons. For that reason, it had to be assumed that, along with the four protons, the alpha particle also contained two electrons. These electrons would neutralize two of the positive charges while adding virtually nothing to the mass.

For about thirty years this proton-electron combination was believed to be the structure of alpha particles. Similar combinations were believed to make up other massive, positively charged particles. However, this inference created problems. There were theoretical reasons for doubting that the alpha particle could possibly be made up of as many as six smaller particles.

Then, in 1932, in experiments suggested by Rutherford, the English physicist James Chadwick (1891–) discovered a particle just about as massive as the proton, but carrying no electric charge at all. Because it was electrically neutral, it was named the *neutron*.

Werner Karl Heisenberg (1901–), a German physicist, at once suggested that it was not proton-electron combinations that made up the massive, positively charged particles, but proton-neutron combinations. The alpha particle, according to this suggestion, would be made up of two protons and two neutrons for a total positive charge of two and a total mass four times that of a single proton.

Physicists found that an alpha particle made up of four subatomic particles, rather than six, would fit their theories beautifully. The proton-neutron structure has been accepted ever since.

CHAPTER 13

THE NUCLEAR ATOM

Atomic Number

The radiations produced by uranium and thorium were quite feeble, and difficult to work with. This situation was corrected by Mme. Curie. Investigating the radioactivity of uranium minerals, she found some samples of ore of low uranium content that were nevertheless intensely radioactive–more so than if they had been pure uranium.

She reached the conclusion that the ore must contain some element other than uranium that was radioactive. Since she knew all the components of the ore that were present in significant amounts, and since all were known to be non-radioactive, the unknown element could be present only in very small quantities and must, therefore, be extremely radioactive indeed.

During 1898, she and her husband slaved away over quantities of ore, trying to concentrate the radioactivity and isolate the new element. In July, one new element was located and named *polonium*, after Mme. Curie's native Poland, and, in December, a second new element, *radium*.

Radium, in particular, was extremely radioactive, giving off radiations in 300,000 times the quantity that the same weight of uranium did. Furthermore, it was very rare. Out of tons of ore, the Curies managed to obtain only about 1/300th of an ounce of radium.

Other strongly radioactive elements were discovered in tiny traces. In 1899, the French chemist André Louis Debierne (1874–1949) discovered *actinium*. In 1900, the German physicist Friedrich Ernst Dorn (1848–1916) found a radioactive gas which eventually received the name *radon*. It was one of the inert gases (see page 143), fitting below xenon in the periodic table. Finally, in 1917, the German chemists Otto Hahn (1879–) and Lise Meitner (1878–) discovered *protactinium*.

Experimenters could use these rare but extremely radioactive elements in "particle guns." Lead absorbs the radiation. If a bit of material containing one of these elements is placed in a lead-lined box with a hole in it, almost all the particles that come flying off are absorbed by the lead. Some, however, make their way through the hole to compose a thin stream of very many, very energetic particles which can be directed at some target.

It was Rutherford who used such "particle guns" most effectively. Beginning in 1906, he bombarded thin sheets of metal (such as gold) with speeding alpha particles. Most of the alpha particles passed clear through, unaffected and undiverted, recording themselves on the photographic plate behind. There were, however, some particles that were scattered—even through large angles.

Since the gold foil that served as target was two thousand atoms thick, and since most alpha particles passed through untouched, it would seem that the atoms were mostly empty space. Since some alpha particles were deflected sharply, it meant that somewhere in the atom must be a massive, positively charged region, capable of turning back the positively charged alpha particle.

Rutherford therefore evolved the theory of the *nuclear atom.* The atom, he decided, contains a very tiny nucleus at its center, which is positively charged and which contains all the protons (and, it was later discovered, the neutrons, too) of the atom. The *atomic nucleus* has to be very tiny in order to account for the very small fraction of the alpha particles that were deflected, but it must also contain virtually all the mass of the atom.

In the outer regions of the atom are the negatively charged electrons, which are too light to interpose an important barrier to the passage of the alpha particles. Although the protons and alpha particles are as massive as atoms, they are actually bare atomic nuclei. They take up so little room in comparison with the atom that they, too, despite their large mass, may be considered subatomic particles.

Rutherford's nuclear atom lent a new subtlety to the question of the indivisibility of the atom. The central nucleus, which was the heart of the atom, was surrounded and protected by a cloud of electrons. It remained untouched and intact through all chemical changes. It was this seeming permanence of the nucleus that led all experimental evidence prior to the 1890s to appear to suggest the notion of an indivisible atom.

However, the atom did undergo one type of change in ordinary chemical reactions. Much of the electron cloud remained intact, but not all. Some electrons could be removed from the "surface" of the atom, or added to that surface. In this way, the problem of ions, which had puzzled three generations of chemists, was finally solved.

If the nuclear atom is accepted, the next question

is: How does the nuclear atom of one element differ from that of another?

Since Dalton's time, different atoms had been known to differ in mass (see page 73), but how is this difference reflected in the subatomic particles making up the nuclear atom?

The beginnings of an answer came through a study of x-rays. The German physicist Max Theodor Felix von Laue (1879–1960) began, in 1909, to bombard crystals with x-rays. These classic experiments established two vital facts: Crystals consist of atoms arranged in a geometrical structure of regular layers, and these layers scatter x-rays in a set pattern. From the manner in which the x-rays are scattered (or diffracted), the size of the tiny waves (*wavelength*) making up the x-rays can be determined.

Next, the English physicist Charles Glover Barkla (1877–1944) found, in 1911, that when x-rays are scattered by particular elements, they produce beams of x-rays that penetrate matter by characteristic amounts. Each element gives rise to a particular set of *characteristic x-rays*. Another English physicist, Henry Gwyn-Jeffreys Moseley (1887–1915), used Laue's method to determine the wavelengths of these characteristic x-rays. He found, in 1913, that the wavelength of these x-rays decreased smoothly with the increasing atomic weight of the elements emitting them. This inverse relationship, Moseley argued, depended on the size of the positive charge on the nucleus of the atom. The larger the charge, the shorter the wavelength of the characteristic x-rays.

From the wavelength, in fact, it was possible to calculate what the charge must be for the atoms of any particular element. Thus, as was eventually shown, hydrogen had a nuclear charge of +1, helium of +2, lithium of +3, and so on all the way up to +92 for uranium.[1]

The size of the nuclear charge is called the *atomic number*. For the first time it was understood that when Mendeléev had arranged his elements in order of what was taken to be atomic weight, he really was arranging them in order of atomic number. In the couple of cases in which he had placed the more massive atoms ahead of less massive ones (see page 134), the less massive one nevertheless had the larger atomic number for reasons which will shortly be discussed.

Now it was finally possible to replace Boyle's operational definition of an element, as a substance that could not be broken down into simpler substances, with a structural definition. The twentieth-century definition of an element would be: An element is a substance consisting of atoms that all possess an identical and characteristic atomic number.

For the first time, also, it became possible to predict exactly how many elements remained to be discovered. All the atomic numbers from 1 to 92 were already occupied by known elements in 1913, except for seven–atomic numbers 43, 61, 72, 75, 85, 87, and 91. In 1917, protactinium (atomic number 91) was discovered. In 1923, *hafnium* (atomic number 72) was discovered, and in 1925, *rhenium* (atomic number 75). Exactly four gaps were left then in the periodic table: 43, 61, 85, and 87. Only four elements, it would seem, remained to be discovered; but those gaps remained well into the 1930s (see page 245).

Since the proton is the only positively charged par-

[1] These numbers are based on a standard according to which the charge on a proton is arbitrarily set equal to +1, and that on an electron to −1.

ticle to be found in the nucleus, the atomic number is equal to the number of protons in the nucleus. Aluminum, with an atomic number of 13, has to contain 13 protons in its nucleus. But since its atomic weight is 27, it must also contain (as was later discovered) 14 neutrons in its nucleus. The neutrons contribute to the mass but not to the charge. In the same way, a sodium atom with an atomic number of 11 and an atomic weight of 23 must have a nucleus with 11 protons and 12 neutrons. (Because protons and neutrons are both found in the nucleus, they are lumped together as *nucleons.*)

The atom in its normal state is electrically neutral. This means that for every proton in the nucleus there must be an electron in the outskirts. Therefore, the number of electrons in the neutral atom is equal to the atomic number. A hydrogen atom contains 1 electron, a sodium atom 11 electrons, a uranium atom 92 electrons, and so on.[2]

Electron Shells

When two atoms collide and react, they either cling together, sharing a number of electrons, or separate again after having transferred one or more electrons from one atom to the other. It is this sharing or transferring of electrons that results in the changes of property noted in the substances undergoing chemical reactions.

A certain amount of order with respect to the manner in which such electron changes occur began to appear from the careful work that was done with the characteristic x-rays. Out of this work arose the

[2] Of course, positive ions have lost electrons and negative ions have gained them. A sodium ion, therefore, has fewer electrons than its atomic number, while a chloride ion has more electrons than its atomic number.

concept that the electrons in an atom existed in groups that might be pictured as *electron shells*. The shells can be visualized as enclosing the nucleus like the rings in an onion, each successive shell capable of holding more electrons than the ones within. The shells were lettered K, L, M, N, and so on.

The innermost shell, the K-shell, can hold only two electrons, the L-shell can hold eight, the M-shell as many as eighteen, and so on. This concept, finally, served to explain the periodic table.

The three electrons of the lithium atom, for instance, are arranged 2,1 among the electron shells; the eleven electrons of the sodium atom are arranged 2,8,1; the nineteen electrons of the potassium atoms are arranged 2,8,8,1; and so on. Each of the alkali metals has the electrons of its atoms so arranged that the outermost occupied electron shell contains just one electron.

Since it is the outermost electron shell that makes contact in collisions between atoms, it is the number of electrons in that outermost shell that would be expected to determine the chemical activity of an element. Different elements with the outermost electron shells similar would have related properties. It is for this reason that the various alkali metals are so similar in their properties.

In the same way, the alkaline earth elements (magnesium, calcium, strontium, and barium) are all similar, for each possesses two electrons in the outermost shell. The halogens (fluorine, chlorine, bromine, and iodine) all possess seven electrons in the outermost shell; while the inert gases (neon, argon, krypton, and xenon) all possess eight.

Indeed, Mendeléev, in arranging his periodic table, had—without knowing it, of course—placed the elements into rows and columns in accordance with the arrangement of their atoms among the electron shells.

As more and more electrons are to be found in the heavier atoms, the electron shells begin to overlap. Atoms of successive atomic numbers have added electrons to an inner shell, but the number of electrons in the outermost shell has remained constant. This configuration happens, in particular, with the rare earth elements, the atomic numbers of which range from 57 to 71 inclusive. While we find an increase in inner shell electrons as we go up the periodic table, all the rare earths retain three electrons in the outermost shell. That similarity of outermost shells explained, at last, why the elements of this group were so unexpectedly similar in their properties.

Mendeléev had arranged his periodic table by considering the valence of the different elements, rather than their electronic arrangements, which were unknown to him. It seemed reasonable, then, to suppose that the valence of an element was governed by its electronic arrangement.

The German chemist Richard Abegg (1869–1910) had pointed out, in 1904, that the inert gases must have a particularly stable electronic configuration. The inert gas atoms had no tendency to add to or subtract from this number, and that was why they did not participate in chemical reactions. It followed that other atoms might give up or accept electrons in order to achieve the inert gas configuration.

Thus, sodium's eleven electrons are 2,8,1 while chlorine's seventeen electrons are 2,8,7. If sodium gives up an electron and chlorine accepts one, the former achieves the 2,8 configuration of neon and the latter the 2,8,8 configuration of argon.

The sodium atom, in giving up a negatively charged electron, is left, of course, with a positive charge and becomes the sodium ion. The chlorine atom in gaining an electron gains a negative charge and becomes the chloride ion. The two tend to cling together by virtue of electric attraction between positive and negative, as Berzelius had suspected a century earlier (see page 106).

It is clear, from this consideration, why sodium should have a valence of 1. It cannot give up more than one electron without breaking up the stable 2,8 arrangement. Nor can the chlorine atom accept more than one electron. On the other hand, calcium, with a 2,8,8,2 arrangement, tends to give up two electrons, and oxygen, with a 2,6 arrangement, tends to accept two electrons. Both elements naturally have a valence of 2.

It is these electron shifts, by the way, that make it possible to set up concentrations of charge in one place or another, so that chemical reactions can serve as a source for electric current, as Volta had discovered over a century earlier (see page 78).

From the electronic view, equivalent weight turned out to represent the relative weights of elements involved in a single electron shift of this sort. The equivalent weight is, after all, the atomic weight divided by the valence (see page 111) or, in other words, the atomic weight divided by the number of electrons transferred.

Abegg's suggestion, however, only considered complete transfers of electrons from one atom to another, producing electrically charged ions which then held together by electrostatic attraction. This is *electrovalence*. Two American chemists, Gilbert Newton Lewis (1875–1946) and Irving Langmuir (1881–1957), independently extended this notion in the years following 1916. They suggested an explanation, for instance, for the structure of the chlorine molecule, in which two chlorine atoms are tightly bound together. Surely, there is no reason for one chlorine atom to transfer an electron to another chlorine atom, and surely they could not hold together by ordinary electrostatic attraction. Both Berzelius's and Abegg's theories of interatomic attractions fall short here.

The Lewis-Langmuir suggestion was, instead, that each atom could contribute an electron to a shared pool. The two electrons in the shared pool remained in the outermost electron shell of both atoms. The electron arrangement in the chlorine molecule might therefore be pictured as: $2,8,6,{}^{1}_{1},6,8,2$ with both shared electrons counting as part of the electron complement in each atom. Each atom would then have the 2,8,8 configuration in place of the much less stable 2,8,7 arrangement of the individual chlorine atoms. It is for that reason that the chlorine molecule is much more stable than are the free atoms.

In order to keep the electron pool in the outermost electron shell of both atoms, the two atoms had to remain in contact, and it takes considerable energy to tear them apart. Each electron contributed to such a pool represents a valence of 1 for the atom doing the contributing. Such valence, requiring the action of two atoms in cooperation, is *covalence.*

The Lewis-Langmuir theory was especially convenient for organic compounds, since the bonds between one carbon atom and another or between one carbon atom and a hydrogen atom were easily explained in this fashion. Most organic molecules could therefore easily be represented by *electronic formulas* where, in general, the old dash of the Kekulé formula (see page 112) was replaced by a shared electron pair.

In fact, the English chemist Nevil Vincent Sidgwick (1873–1952) was able, in the 1920s, to extend the notion of electron-pair covalence to inorganic compounds. In particular, he applied them to Werner's coordination compounds (see page 121) where the ordinary Kekulé representations were difficult to apply.

In all these chemical changes only electrons are being shifted. The protons (in all but one case) are safely protected in the central nucleus. The exceptional case is that of hydrogen, which has a nucleus made up of a single proton. If the hydrogen atom is ionized through removal of its single electron, the proton is left bare.[3]

In 1923, the Danish chemist Johannes Nicolaus Brønsted (1879–1947) introduced a new view of acids and bases (see page 70). An acid was defined as a compound tending to give up a proton (or hydrogen ion), while a base was one tending to combine with a proton. This new view accounted for all the facts already satisfactorily accounted for by the old view. In addition, however, it represented a greater flexibility that made it possible to extend acid-base notions into areas in which the old view was inadequate.

Resonance

The relatively small molecules and rapid, ionic reactions in inorganic chemistry had proven comparatively easy to study. Chemists, from Lavoisier's time onward, could predict the course of such reactions

[3] Such a bare proton is very active and does not remain bare for long. In water solution, it immediately attaches itself to a water molecule, adding a positively charged hydrogen atom to that molecule. Thus is formed the *oxonium ion* (H_3O^+).

and the manner of modifying them to suit needs. The complicated molecules and slow reactions in organic chemistry were much harder to analyze. Often there were several ways in which two substances could react; guiding the reaction into some desired path was a matter of art and intuition rather than of secure knowledge.

The electronic atom, however, offered organic chemists a new look at their field. In the late 1920s, men such as the English chemist Christopher Ingold (1893–) began to try to interpret organic reactions in terms of electron shifts from point to point within a molecule. The methods of physical chemistry began to be applied intensively in an attempt to interpret the directions and tendencies of such shifts. *Physical organic chemistry* became an important discipline.

It proved insufficient, however, to attempt to interpret organic reactions in terms of hard little electrons moving here and there, and it did not long remain necessary to do so.

For the first quarter-century after the discovery of the electron, it was taken for granted that the particle was a tiny, hard sphere. In 1923, however, Louis Victor, Prince de Broglie, a French physicist (1892–), had presented theoretical reasons for considering electrons (and all other particles as well) to possess wave properties. Before the end of the 1920s this view had been confirmed by experiment.

Pauling (the first to suggest the helical shape of proteins and nucleic acids, see page 179) thereupon developed methods, in the early 1930s, for taking into account the wave nature of electrons in considering organic reactions. He showed that the Lewis-Langmuir electron pool could be interpreted as wave-interactions. Electron waves paired off in reinforcement, resonating with each other to form a stabler situation in combination than in separation.

This *theory of resonance* was particularly useful in establishing the structure of benzene, which had been puzzling in Kekulé's day (see page 100) and which had retained questionable points ever since. As usually drawn, the structure of benzene is that of a hexagon with alternating single bonds and double bonds. By the Lewis-Langmuir system, two-electron pools and four-electron pools alternated. Benzene, however, lacked almost completely the characteristic properties of other compounds which contained double bonds, or four-electron pools.

Pauling showed that if electrons were regarded as wave-forms, the individual electrons need not be considered as occupying a single point, but could "smear out" over a considerable area. The "electron waves" could spread out, in other words, to take up far larger areas than a tiny "billiard ball" electron could be expected to take up. The tendency to "smear" in this fashion was accentuated if a molecule was quite flat and symmetrical.

The benzene molecule is flat and symmetrical, and Pauling showed that the electrons "smeared out" in such a fashion that all six carbon atoms of the benzene ring were bound in equal fashion. The bonds connecting them could not be represented as either single bonds or double bonds, but as a kind of particularly stable average, or *resonance hybrid,* between the two extremes.

Other points besides the structure of benzene were clarified by the theory of resonance. For instance, the four electrons in the outermost shell of the carbon atom are not all equivalent from the standpoint of energy characteristics. It might have been assumed, then, that bonds of slightly different type would be formed between a carbon atom and its neighbor, depending on which of carbon's electrons was involved.

It could be shown, though, that the four electrons, as wave-forms, interacted and formed four "average" bonds that were precisely equivalent, and directed toward the apices of a tetrahedron. Thus, the Van't Hoff-Le Bel tetrahedral atom (see page 120) was explained in electronic terms.

Resonance also helped to explain a group of strange compounds that had first impinged on the chemical consciousness at the opening of the twentieth century. In 1900, the Russian-American chemist Moses Gomberg (1866–1947) was trying to prepare hexaphenylethane, a compound with a molecule consisting of two carbon atoms to which six benzene rings were attached (three per carbon atom).

He obtained, instead, a colored solution of a very reactive compound. For various reasons, he was forced to conclude that he had obtained *triphenylmethyl,* a "half-molecule" consisting of a carbon atom with three benzene rings attached. The fourth valence bond of the carbon atom remained unused. Such a compound resembled one of the old radicals (see page 104) torn loose from a molecule. It was therefore termed a *free radical.*

Once the electronic atom was introduced, a free radical such as triphenylmethyl was understood to contain an unpaired electron in the place where the old Kekulé view would have put an unused bond. Ordinarily, such an unpaired electron is highly unstable. However, if a molecule is flat and highly symmetrical, as triphenylmethyl is, the unused electron can be "smeared out" over the entire molecule. The free radical is then stabilized.

When organic reactions came to be studied in electronic terms, it became clear that there were usually stages where a free radical had to be formed.

Such free radicals, generally not stabilized by resonance, could exist only momentarily and could be formed only with difficulty. It was the difficulty of forming free radical intermediates that made most organic reactions so slow.

In the second quarter of the twentieth century, organic chemists were beginning to get considerable insight into the detailed steps that made up organic reactions—the reaction mechanism, in other words. It was this insight, more than anything else, which has guided contemporary organic chemists in their synthetic work and has led to the syntheses of molecules whose complexities had defeated earlier generations.

Nor were resonance considerations confined to organic chemistry alone. The boron hydrides possessed molecules that could not be neatly represented by older views. The boron atom possessed too few valence bonds (or electrons) for the purpose. Yet if the electrons were properly "smeared" as wave forms, a reasonable molecular structure could be proposed.

Again, in 1932, Pauling reasoned that the inert gas atoms could not be as resistant to forming bonds as had been assumed for the third of a century that had elapsed since their discovery. Under sufficient pressure by an extremely reactive atom such as that of fluorine, compounds might be formed.

This suggestion of Pauling's went unheeded at first, but in 1962, *xenon fluoride* was formed by reacting the inert gas xenon with fluorine. In short order a number of xenon compounds with fluorine and with oxygen were formed, as well as one or two of radon and of krypton.

Half-Life

If the studies of the internal atomic structure had led to new insights and understandings, they also posed a normal share of new problems.

In 1900, Crookes (see page 202) had discovered that freshly prepared pure uranium compounds were only very slightly radioactive, but that their radioactivity strengthened on standing. By 1902 Rutherford and a co-worker, the English chemist Frederick Soddy (1877–1956), proposed that as a uranium atom gave off an alpha particle, its nature changed. It became a new type of atom, with different radioactive characteristics, producing stronger radiations than uranium itself (thus accounting for Crookes's observation).

This second atom in turn broke down, forming still another type of atom. Indeed, the uranium atom was the parent of a whole series of radioactive elements, a *radioactive series,* that included radium and polonium (see page 214) and ended finally with lead, which was not radioactive. It was for this reason that radium, polonium, and other rare radioactive elements could be found in uranium minerals. A second radioactive series also began with uranium, while a third series began with thorium.

(This breakdown of uranium into lead would, by Boyle's definition of elements, have made it necessary to view uranium as not being an element. By the new atomic number definition, however, it was still an element. It is just that since atoms are not really indivisible particles after all, elements are not necessarily entirely unchangeable. This represents a return–on a much higher level of sophistication–to the old alchemical concept.)

It is reasonable to ask why, though, if radioactive elements are constantly breaking down, any remained in existence at all? It was Rutherford who, in 1904, solved this matter. In studying the rate of radioactive breakdown, he was able to show that after a certain period, which was different for each element, half of any given quantity of a certain radioactive element would have broken down. This period, which is characteristic for each particular type of radioactive substance, Rutherford called the *half-life*. (See Figure 22.)

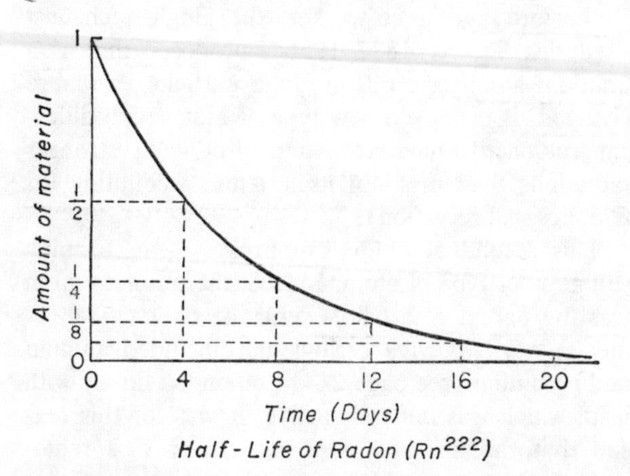

FIG. 22. Half-life of radon is determined by measuring amounts of material remaining after equal intervals of time. The plot is the exponential "dieaway" curve, $y = e^{-ax}$.

The half-life of radium, for instance, is just under 1600 years. Over the geological eras any radium in the earth's crust would certainly have long since vanished, were it not that new supplies are constantly being formed through the breakdown of uranium. The same is true for other breakdown products of uranium, some of which have half-lives of only fractions of a second.

As for uranium itself, that has a half-life of 4,500,000,000 years. This is a tremendous period of time, and in all the history of the earth, only a fraction of the original supply of uranium has had a chance to break down. Thorium breaks down even more slowly, its half-life being 14,000,000,000 years.

Such huge stretches of time can be determined by counting the number of alpha particles produced by a given mass of uranium (or thorium). The alpha particles were counted by Rutherford, by noting the small flashes they made when they struck a screen of zinc sulfide. (This was a *scintillation counter.*)

Each alpha particle given off meant a uranium atom breaking down so that Rutherford could determine how many atoms were breaking down per second. From the mass of the uranium he was dealing with, he knew the total number of uranium atoms present. With this information, he could easily calculate how long it would take for half the uranium atoms present to break down, and it turned out to be a matter of billions of years.

So constant and characteristic is the majestically slow decay of uranium that it can be used to measure the age of the earth. In 1907, the American chemist Bertram Borden Boltwood (1870–1927) suggested that the lead content of uranium minerals would serve as guide in this respect. If it is assumed that all the lead in the mineral originated from uranium decay, it would be easy to calculate how long a time must have elapsed to bring that amount of lead into existence. It was eventually calculated in this way that the solid crust of the earth must have been in existence for at least four billion years.

Meanwhile, Soddy had gone on to describe the exact manner in which an atom changed as it gave off subatomic particles. If an atom lost an alpha particle, with a charge of +2, the total charge on its nucleus was decreased by two. The atom moved two places to the left in the periodic table.

If an atom lost a beta particle (an electron with a charge of −1), the nucleus gained an additional positive charge[4] and the element moved one place to the right in the periodic table. If an atom lost a gamma ray (uncharged), its energy content was altered but there was no change in its particle make-up, so that it remained the same element.

Using these rules as a guide, chemists could work out the details of the various radioactive series.

Isotopes

But all this raised a serious problem. What was one to do with the various breakdown products of uranium and thorium? Dozens of these were discovered, but there were at most only nine places in the periodic table (from polonium at atomic number 84 to uranium at atomic number 92) in which to place them.

As a specific example, the uranium atom (atomic number 92) emitted an alpha particle and the atomic number of what was left of the atom therefore became 90, by Soddy's rule. This meant that a thorium atom had been formed. However, whereas ordinary thorium had a half-life of 14 billion years, the thorium produced from uranium had a half-life of 24 days.

[4] In Soddy's time, it was felt that there were electrons in the nucleus and that the loss of a beta particle from the nucleus left an additional proton unbalanced, hence raised the positive charge. Nowadays, it is felt that the nucleus contains only protons and neutrons, but that an electron is formed and expelled when a neutron is converted into a proton, for the gain of a positive charge is equivalent to the loss, by expulsion, of a negative charge.

Differences existed even in the case of non-radioactive elements and in properties not involving radioactivity. For instance, Richards (the expert on atomic weights, see page 85) was able to show, in 1913, that the lead produced by the decay of uranium did not have quite the same atomic weight as ordinary lead.

Soddy advanced the bold suggestion that more than one kind of atom could fit into the same place in the periodic table. Place number 90 might hold different varieties of thorium, place number 82 different varieties of lead, and so on. He called these atom-varieties occupying the same place *isotopes,* from the Greek word meaning "same place."

The different isotopes in a given place in the table would have the same atomic number, therefore the same number of protons in the nucleus and the same number of electrons in the outskirts. The isotopes of an element would have the same chemical properties, since these properties depend on the number and arrangement of the electrons in the atoms.

But in that case, how explain differences in radioactive properties and in atomic weight?

Atomic weight might represent the key to the difference. A hundred years earlier, Prout had advanced his famous hypothesis (see page 84) that all atoms are composed of hydrogen so that all elements should have integral atomic weight. The fact that most atomic weights are not integers seemed to have destroyed his hypothesis.

But now the atom, in its new nuclear guise, had to be made up of protons (and neutrons). Protons and neutrons are about equally massive, and therefore, all atoms had to have weights that were integral multiples of the weight of hydrogen (made up of a single proton). Prout's hypothesis was reinstated, and a look of new suspicion was directed at the atomic weights instead.

In 1912, J. J. Thomson (the discoverer of the electron) had subjected beams of positively charged neon ions to the action of a magnetic field. The field deflected the neon ions and caused them to fall on a photographic plate. If all the ions had been identical in mass they would all have been deflected by the same amount, and a single discolored spot on the photographic film would have appeared. However, two spots were located, one some ten times as dark as the other. A co-worker, Francis William Aston (1877–1945), later improved the device and confirmed the results. Similar results were uncovered for other elements. Since this device separated chemically similar ions into a kind of spectrum of dark spots, it was called the *mass spectrograph.*

The extent of deflection of ions of identical charge by a magnetic field depends upon the mass of the ion; the more massive the ion, the less it is deflected. From the results obtained by Thomson and Aston it would seem, therefore, that there were two kinds of neon atoms, one more massive than the other. One type had a *mass number* of 20 and the other, one of 22. Since the neon-20 was ten times as common as neon-22, judging from the relative darkness of the spots (in later years tiny quantities of neon-21 were also located), it was reasonable that the atomic weight of neon was about 20.2.

In other words, individual atoms had masses that were an integral multiple of that of the hydrogen atom,[5] but a particular element, being made up of

[5] Not quite a multiple, in actual fact. The small deviations in mass are of no importance in chemistry but are a reflection of the huge energies involved in nuclear forces—energies that have been made manifest in nuclear bombs (see page 253).

atoms of different mass, would have an atomic weight that was a weighted average of these integers and would therefore not necessarily be an integer itself.

The weighted average of the isotopes of a particular atom may be greater, in some cases, than the weighted average for an atom of higher atomic number.

For instance, tellurium, with an atomic number of 52, consists of seven isotopes. Of these, the two most massive isotopes, tellurium-126 and tellurium-128, are the most common. The atomic weight of tellurium therefore comes to 127.6. Iodine has the next higher atomic number, 53, but it is made up of iodine-127 only and therefore has the atomic weight of 127. When Mendeléev placed iodine after tellurium in his periodic table, reversing the order dictated by atomic weight, he was, without knowing it, following atomic number instead; and this was the correct thing to do.

Here's another example. Potassium (atomic number 19) is made up of three isotopes, potassium-39, potassium-40, and potassium-41, but the lightest isotope, potassium-39, is by far the most common. Hence, the atomic weight of potassium is 39.1. Argon has a lower atomic number (18) and is made up of three isotopes also, argon-36, argon-38, and argon-40. Here, however, it is the most massive isotope, argon-40, which is most common. Therefore the atomic weight of argon is about 40. When Ramsay placed argon before potassium instead of after (see page 142) in defiance of atomic weights, he, too, without knowing it, was following atomic number and was doing the correct thing.

The use of the mass spectrograph made it possible to determine atomic weight by actually measuring the mass of the individual isotopes and the quantity of each present—and then taking the average. This method surpassed chemical methods for measuring atomic weight in accuracy.

Different isotopes of a given element have the same atomic number but different mass numbers. The different isotopes would have the same number of protons in their nucleus but different numbers of neutrons. Thus, neon-20, neon-21, and neon-22 all have 10 protons in the nucleus, so that all have an atomic number of 10, and all have an electron arrangement of 2,8. However, neon-20 has a nucleus containing 10 protons plus 10 neutrons; neon-21, one containing 10 protons plus 11 neutrons; and neon-22, one containing 10 protons plus 12 neutrons.

Most elements (but not all) could be divided into isotopes in this manner. In 1935, the Canadian-American physicist Arthur Jeffrey Dempster (1886–1950) found, for instance, that uranium, as it occurred in nature, was a mixture of two isotopes even though its atomic weight (238.07) was close to a whole number. It was just that one isotope existed in overwhelming proportion. Fully 99.3 per cent of the uranium atoms had nuclei made up of 92 protons and 146 neutrons or a total mass number of 238. These were uranium-238 atoms. The remaining 0.7 per cent, however, had three fewer neutrons and were uranium-235 atoms.

Since radioactive properties depend upon the constitution of the atomic nucleus, and not upon electron arrangement, the isotopes of an element might be similar chemically, but quite different from the standpoint of radioactivity. Thus, whereas uranium-238 had a half-life of 4,500,000,000 years, that of uranium-235 was only 700,000,000 years.[6] Both are parents of separate radioactive series, too.

There were theoretical reasons for suspecting that hydrogen itself, the simplest element, might be made up of a pair of isotopes. Ordinary hydrogen atoms, with nuclei composed of a single proton, make up hydrogen-1. In 1931, however, the American chemist Harold Clayton Urey (1893–) slowly evaporated four liters of liquid hydrogen on the presumption that if any heavier isotope of hydrogen existed, it would have a higher boiling point and would evaporate more slowly. This meant it would remain behind and accumulate in the residue.

Sure enough, in the final cubic centimeter of hydrogen Urey was able to detect unmistakable signs of the existence of hydrogen-2, the nucleus of which consisted of one proton plus one neutron. Hydrogen-2 received the special name of *deuterium.*

Nor was oxygen immune. In 1929, the American chemist William Francis Giauque (1895–) succeeded in showing that oxygen was made up of three isotopes. The most common variety, comprising nearly 99.8 per cent of all the atoms, was oxygen-16. Its nucleus contained 8 protons plus 8 neutrons. The rest were almost all oxygen-18 (8 protons plus 10 neutrons) with a trace of oxygen-17 (8 protons plus 9 neutrons).

This created a problem. Ever since the days of Berzelius, the atomic weights had been based on the arbitrary assignment of a weight of 16.0000 to the oxygen atom (see page 85). But the atomic weight of oxygen could be only the weighted average of

[6] This accounts also for the difference, mentioned earlier (see page 232) in the half-lives of natural thorium (thorium-232) and the thorium formed from the breakdown of uranium (thorium-234) which contains two additional neutrons in each nucleus.

the three isotopes, and the proportion of the isotopes in oxygen might vary slightly from sample to sample.

The physicists took to determining atomic weights on the basis of oxygen-16 set equal to 16.0000, and this gave them a series of values (the *physical atomic weight*) that were uniformly greater, by a very small amount, than the values that had been used and gradually improved throughout the nineteenth century (the *chemical atomic weights*).

In 1961, however, international organizations of both chemists and of physicists agreed to adopt an atomic weight standard based on carbon-12 set equal to exactly 12.0000. This new standard was almost exactly that of the old chemical atomic weights and yet it was tied to a single isotope and not to the average of a group of them.

Chapter 14

NUCLEAR REACTIONS

The New Transmutation

Once it was understood that the atom was made up of smaller particles, which rearranged themselves spontaneously in radioactive transformations, the next step seemed almost ordained.

Man could deliberately rearrange the atomic structure of molecules in ordinary chemical reactions. Why not, then, deliberately rearrange the protons and neutrons of the atomic nucleus in *nuclear reactions?* To be sure, the protons and neutrons are bound together by forces far stronger than those binding atoms in molecules, and methods that sufficed to bring about ordinary reactions would not suffice for nuclear reactions, but the men who had solved the puzzle of radioactivity were traveling the high road of success.

It was Rutherford who took the first step. He bombarded various gases with alpha particles and found that every once in a while an alpha particle would strike the nucleus of an atom and disarrange it. (See Figure 23.)

In fact, Rutherford was able to demonstrate, in 1919, that alpha particles could knock protons out of nitrogen nuclei and merge with what was left behind. The most common isotope of nitrogen is nitrogen-14, which has a nucleus made up of 7 pro-

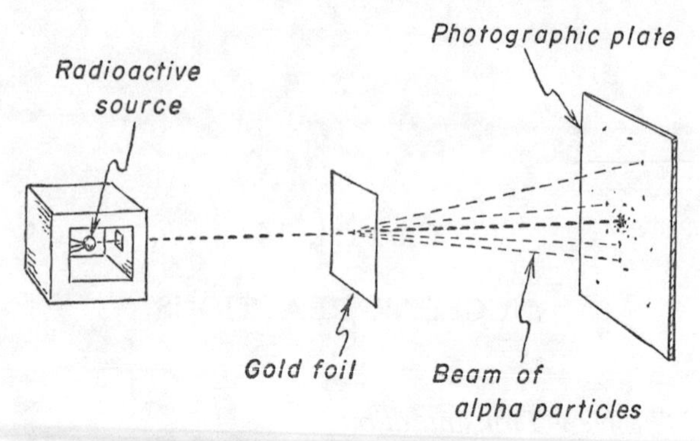

FIG. 23. Rutherford experiment led to concept of nucleus and opened the door to modern nuclear physics. Alpha particles emitted from radioactive source were deflected when passing through gold foil. Amount of deflection was recorded when particles struck the photographic plate.

tons and 7 neutrons. Subtract a proton and add the 2 protons and 2 neutrons of the alpha particle and you end with a nucleus possessing 8 protons and 9 neutrons. This is oxygen-17. The alpha particle can be considered as helium-4 and the proton as hydrogen-1.

It follows then that Rutherford had successfully carried through the first manmade nuclear reaction:

nitrogen-14 + helium-4 → oxygen-17 + hydrogen-1

This is a true example of transmutation, the conversion of one element to another. In a way, it was the climax of the old alchemical longings but, of course, it involved elements and techniques of which the alchemists had never dreamed.

Over the next five years, Rutherford carried through a number of other nuclear reactions involving alpha particles. What he could do was limited, however, for radioactive elements provided alpha particles of only moderate energies. To accomplish more, much more energetic particles were required.

Physicists took to designing devices to accelerate charged particles in an electric field, forcing them to move faster and faster and therefore to possess more and more energy. The English physicist John Douglas Cockcroft (1897–) and his co-worker, the Irish physicist Ernest Thomas Sinton Walton (1903–), were the first to design an accelerator capable of producing particles energetic enough to carry through a nuclear reaction, accomplishing this in 1929. Three years later, they bombarded lithium atoms with accelerated protons and produced alpha particles. The nuclear reaction was:

$$\text{hydrogen-1} + \text{lithium-7} \rightarrow \text{helium-4} + \text{helium-4}$$

In the Cockcroft-Walton device, and in others that were being planned, the particles were accelerated in a straight line, and it was difficult to build devices long enough to produce extremely high energies. In 1930, the American physicist Ernest Orlando Lawrence (1901–58) designed an accelerator that forced the particles to travel in a slowly expanding spiral. A relatively small *cyclotron* of this sort could produce highly energetic particles.

Lawrence's first tiny cyclotron was the ancestor of today's huge instruments half a mile in circumference, which have been used to probe for answers to the fundamental questions concerning the structure of matter.

In 1930, the English physicist Paul Adrien Maurice Dirac (1902–) had advanced theoretical reasons for supposing that both protons and electrons ought to have true opposites (*anti-particles*). The *anti-electron* ought to have the mass of an electron but be positively charged, while the *anti-proton* would have the mass of a proton but be negatively charged.

The anti-electron was indeed detected in 1932 by the American physicist Carl David Anderson (1905–), in his study of cosmic rays.[1] When cosmic ray particles strike atomic nuclei in the atmosphere, some particles are produced that curve in a magnetic field just as electrons do, but in the opposite direction. Anderson named the particle of this sort the *positron*.

The anti-proton defied detection for another quarter-century. Since the anti-proton is 1836 times as massive as the anti-electron, 1836 times as much energy is required for its formation. The necessary energies were not created in manmade devices until the 1950s. Using huge accelerators, the Italian-American physicist Emilio Segré (1905–) and his co-worker, the American physicist Owen Chamberlain (1920–), were able to produce and detect the anti-proton in 1955.

It has been pointed out that atoms might well exist in which negatively charged nuclei, containing anti-protons, are surrounded by positively charged positrons. Such *anti-matter* could not exist for long on the earth or, perhaps, anywhere in our galaxy, for on contact both matter and anti-matter would be annihilated in a great lash of energy. However, astronomers wonder if there may not be whole galaxies built of anti-matter. If so, they might be most difficult to detect.

[1] Cosmic rays consist of particles entering earth's atmosphere from outer space. The particles (mostly protons) are sped to almost unimaginable energies by acceleration across the electric fields associated with the stars and with the galaxy itself.

Artificial Radioactivity

The first nuclear reactions carried through successfully produced isotopes already known to occur in nature. This, however, was not inevitable. Suppose a neutron-proton combination not occurring in nature were to be produced, as, a century earlier (see page 95), organic molecules not occurring in nature had been produced. This phenomenon was, indeed, accomplished in 1934, by the husband-wife team of French physicists, Frédéric Joliot-Curie (1900–58) and Irène Joliot-Curie (1897–1956), the latter being the daughter of the Curies (page 211) of radium fame.

The Joliot-Curies were bombarding aluminum with alpha particles. After they had ceased the bombardment, they discovered that the aluminum continued to radiate particles of its own. They had begun, they discovered, with aluminum-27 (13 protons plus 14 neutrons) and ended with phosphorus-30 (15 protons plus 15 neutrons).

But phosphorus, as it occurs in nature, is made up of one atom variety only, phosphorus-31 (15 protons plus 16 neutrons). Phosphorus-30, therefore, was an artificial isotope, one that did not occur in nature. The reason it did not occur in nature was clear; it was radioactive, with a half-life of only 14 days. Its radioactivity was the source of the continuing particle radiation the Joliot-Curies had observed.

The Joliot-Curies had produced the first case of *artificial radioactivity*. Since 1934 over a thousand isotopes not occurring in nature have been formed, and every one of them is radioactive. Every element possesses one or more radioactive isotopes. Even hydrogen has one, hydrogen-3 (also called *tritium*) with a half-life of 12 years.

An unusual radioactive carbon isotope, carbon-14, was discovered in 1940 by the Canadian-American chemist Martin D. Kamen (1913–). Some of this isotope is formed by cosmic ray bombardment of the nitrogen in the atmosphere. This means that we are always breathing some carbon-14 and incorporating it into our tissues, as all life-forms do. Once a life-form dies, the incorporation ceases and the carbon-14 already present slowly decays away.

Carbon-14 has a half-life of over 5000 years, so that significant amounts linger on in material (wood, textiles) dating back to prehistoric times. The American chemist Willard Frank Libby (1908–) devised a technique for dating archaeological remains by their carbon-14 content as the earth's crust can be dated by uranium and lead contents (see page 231). Thus, chemistry has come to be of direct use to historians and archaeologists.

Chemicals can be synthesized with unusual isotopes incorporated in place of the ordinary ones. These might be the rare stable isotopes, for instance (hydrogen-2 in place of hydrogen-1, carbon-13 in place of carbon-12, nitrogen-15 in place of nitrogen-14, or oxygen-18 in place of oxygen-16). If animals eat such *tagged compounds* and are later killed and their tissues analyzed, the compounds in which the isotopes are found yield significant information. It becomes possible to deduce reaction mechanisms within living tissue that might otherwise go undetected. An innovator in this sort of work was the German-American biochemist Rudolf Schoenheimer (1898–1941), who performed important researches on fats and proteins using hydrogen-2 and nitrogen-15 in the years after 1935. The use of radioactive isotopes makes it possible to trace reactions even more delicately, but it was not until after World War II that such isotopes became available in quantity. An example of what can be done with isotopes was the work of the American biochemist Melvin Calvin (1911–). He used carbon-14 during the 1950s to work out many of the reactions involved in the process of photosynthesis. He did this with a detail that would have been deemed wildly impossible only twenty years earlier.

Nor was it merely artificial isotopes that were formed. Artificial elements were formed also. In 1937, Lawrence, the inventor of the cyclotron, had bombarded a sample of molybdenum (atomic number 42) with deuterons (nuclei of hydrogen-2). He sent the bombarded sample to Segré in Rome. (Later Segré was to come to the United States and in his new home was to discover the anti-proton.)

Segré, on close study, found the sample to contain traces of a new radioactive substance, which turned out to be atoms of the element with atomic number 43. At the time that element had not been discovered in nature (despite some false alarms) and so it was named *technetium,* from a Greek word meaning "artificial."

Eventually the three remaining gaps in the periodic table (see page 218) were filled. In 1939 and 1940, elements number 87 (*francium*) and 85 (*astatine*) were discovered, and in 1947, the last gap, that of element number 61 (*promethium*) was plugged. All these elements are radioactive.

Astatine and francium are formed from uranium only in most minute quantities, the scarcity explaining why they were not discovered earlier. Technetium and promethium are formed in even smaller quantities, and are unusual in that they are the only elements of atomic number less than 84 which possess no stable isotopes at all.

Transuranium Elements

The first particles used to bombard atomic nuclei were positively charged—the proton, deuteron, and alpha particle. Such positively charged particles are pushed away by the positively charged atomic nuclei, since among electric charges like repels like. It takes considerable energy to force the speeding particles to overcome the repulsion and strike the nuclei, and so nuclear reactions were rather hard to bring about.

Once the neutron was discovered (see page 212), a new possibility offered itself. Since neutrons were uncharged, the atomic nuclei did not repel them. A neutron could easily strike an atomic nucleus, without resistance, if the neutron happened to be moving in the right direction.

The first to investigate neutron bombardment in detail was the Italian physicist Enrico Fermi (1901–54). He began his work almost immediately upon hearing of the discovery of the neutron. He found that a beam of neutrons was particularly effective in initiating nuclear reactions if it passed through water or paraffin first. The light atoms in these compounds absorbed some of the neutron's energy with each collision and did so without absorbing the neutrons themselves. The neutrons were therefore so slowed down that eventually they moved with only the normal speed of molecules at room temperature. Such *thermal neutrons* stayed in the vicinity of a particular nucleus a longer fraction of a second and were more likely to be absorbed than fast neutrons were.

When a neutron is absorbed into an atomic nucleus, that nucleus does not necessarily become a new element. It may simply become a heavier isotope. Thus, if oxygen-16 gained a neutron (with a mass number of 1) it would become oxygen-17. However, in gaining a neutron an element might become a radioactive isotope. In that case, it would generally break down by emitting a beta particle, and by Soddy's rule that would mean it would become an element one place higher in the periodic table. Thus, if oxygen-18 gained a neutron, it would become radioactive oxygen-19. That isotope would emit a beta particle and become stable fluorine-19. Thus oxygen would be converted (one atomic number higher) by neutron bombardment.

In 1934, it occurred to Fermi to bombard uranium with neutrons to see whether he could produce atoms more massive than uranium (*transuranium elements*). At that time uranium had the highest atomic number in the periodic table, but this could mean merely that elements of higher atomic number had half-lives too short to have survived the earth's long past history.

At first Fermi actually thought he had synthesized some of element number 93, but the results he obtained were confusing and led to something else far more dramatic, as will shortly be described. These other developments distracted attention for a few years from the possible formation of transuranium elements.

In 1940, however, the American physicist Edwin Mattison McMillan (1907–) and his colleague, the chemist Philip Hauge Abelson (1913–), in their work on neutron bombardment of uranium, did indeed detect a new type of atom. On investigation, it proved to be one with an atomic number of 93, and they named it *neptunium*. Even the longest-lived neptunium isotope, neptunium-237, had a half-life of only a little over two million years, not enough to allow it to survive across earth's long history. Neptunium-237 was the ancestor of a fourth radioactive series.

McMillan was then joined by the American physicist Glenn Theodore Seaborg (1912–), and together they formed and identified *plutonium,* element number 94, in 1941. Under the leadership of Seaborg, a group of scientists at the University of California, over the next ten years, isolated a half-dozen more elements: *americium* (number 95), *curium* (number 96), *berkelium* (number 97), *californium* (number 98), *einsteinium* (number 99), and *fermium* (number 100).

There seemed no reason to suppose that any atomic number represented an absolute maximum. However, each succeeding element is harder to form and is produced in smaller quantities. What's more, the half-lives grow shorter so that what is formed vanishes more and more quickly. Nevertheless, in 1955, *mendelevium* (number 101) was formed; in 1957, *nobelium* (number 102), and in 1961, *lawrencium* (number 103). In 1964, Russian physicists reported the preparation of element number 104, in trace amounts.

Seaborg and his group recognized that the transuranium elements resembled each other much as the rare earth elements do (see page 141), and for the same reason. New electrons are added to an inner electron shell, leaving the outermost electron shell with a three-electron content throughout. The two sets of similar elements are distinguished by calling the older one, which begins with lanthanum (atomic number 57) the *lanthanides,* while the newer one, which begins with actinium (atomic number 89), is the *actinides.*

With the discovery of lawrencium, all the actinides had been formed. Element number 104 is expected to have chemical properties quite different from the actinides.

Nuclear Bombs

But what of Fermi's original work on the bombardment of uranium with neutrons? His suspicion that element number 93 had been formed could not be confirmed at that time, for the physicists who labored to isolate it all failed.

Among those joining the investigation were Hahn and Meitner, the discoverers of protactinium twenty years before (page 215). They treated the bombarded uranium with barium, which carried down in precipitation a certain fraction of strongly radioactive material. This reaction made them suspect that one of the products of the bombardment was radium. Radium is very similar, chemically, to barium and would be expected to accompany barium in any chemical manipulations. However, no radium could be obtained from those barium-containing fractions.

By 1938, Hahn began to wonder if it were not a radioactive isotope of barium itself that had been formed from the uranium in the course of neutron bombardment. Such radioactive barium would merge with ordinary barium and the two could not then be separated by ordinary chemical techniques. Such a combination seemed impossible, however. All nuclear reactions known up to 1938 had involved changes in elements of only 1 or 2 units in atomic number. To change uranium to barium meant a decrease, in atomic number, of 36! It was as though the uranium atom had broken more or less in half (*uranium fission*). Hahn hesitated even to speculate on such a possibility—at least, not in public.

In 1938, Nazi Germany invaded and annexed Austria. Lise Meitner, an Austrian, was forced into exile because she was Jewish. From her place of exile in Sweden, the dangers she had undergone must have made those involved in making a scientific error seem small indeed. She published Hahn's theory that uranium atoms when bombarded with neutrons underwent fission.

This paper created great excitement because of the horrendous possibilities it evoked. If a uranium atom, upon absorbing a neutron, breaks into two smaller atoms, those smaller atoms will need fewer neutrons than were originally present in the uranium atom.[2] These superfluous neutrons would be emitted, and if they were absorbed by other uranium atoms, those would also undergo fission and emit still more neutrons.

Each splitting uranium atom would bring about the splitting of several more in a *nuclear chain reaction,* with a result similar to that of an ordinary chemical chain reaction in the case of hydrogen and chlorine (see page 160). But since nuclear reactions involved far greater energy exchanges than chemical reactions did, the results of a nuclear chain reaction would be far more formidable. After beginning with just a few neutrons, involving only the most trifling investment of energy, colossal stores of energy could be released.

World War II was on the point of starting. The United States Government, fearful that the deadly energies of the atomic nucleus might be unleashed by the Nazis, launched a research program to

[2] In general, the more massive an atom the greater the number of neutrons it requires in proportion to its mass number. Thus calcium-40 contains 20 neutrons, 0.5 its mass number; while uranium-238 contains 153 neutrons, 0.65 its mass number.

achieve such a chain reaction and place the weapon in its own hands.

The difficulties were many. As many neutrons as possible had to be made to collide with uranium atoms before escaping out of the uranium altogether. For that reason the uranium had to be quite large in bulk (the necessary size is the *critical mass*) in order to give the neutrons the needed chance. Yet when research began there was very little uranium available, for there had been almost no use for the substance prior to 1940.

Then, too, the neutrons had to be slowed down so as to increase the probability of their being absorbed by uranium. This meant the use of a *moderator,* a substance with light atoms against which the neutrons would bounce. That moderator might be graphite blocks or heavy water.

As a further difficulty, it was not just any uranium atom that underwent fission on absorbing a neutron. It was the rather rare isotope uranium-235 (see page 236). Methods had to be devised to separate and concentrate uranium-235. This was an unprecedented task, for the separation of isotopes on a large scale had never before been carried through. One successful method made use of uranium hexafluoride, which required a massive advance in the handling of fluorine compounds. The manmade element plutonium was found to undergo fission also, and, after it was discovered in 1941 (see page 248), efforts had to be made to produce it in large quantities.

Fermi, who had left Italy in 1938 and had come to the United States, was placed in charge of the task. On December 2, 1942, an *atomic pile* of uranium, uranium oxide, and graphite "went critical." A chain reaction was maintained and energy was produced through uranium fission.

By 1945, devices were prepared in which, when a small charge of explosive was set off, two pieces of uranium were driven together. Each piece by itself was below critical mass, but together they were above it. Thanks to cosmic ray bombardment, the atmosphere always contains stray neutrons, so a nuclear chain reaction starts at once in the critical mass of uranium, which explodes with fury hitherto unimagined.

In July 1945, the first such "atomic bomb" or "A-bomb" (more properly called a *fission bomb*) was exploded in Alamogordo, New Mexico. By the next month, two more bombs were manufactured and were exploded over Hiroshima and Nagasaki in Japan, ending World War II.

Uranium fission is not used exclusively for destruction, however. When the energy production is maintained at a constant, safe level, fission can be put to constructive use. Atomic piles, renamed, more appropriately, *nuclear reactors,* have been built in great numbers during the 1950s and 1960s. They are used to propel submarines and surface vessels, and also to produce energy, in the form of electricity, for civilian use.

Energy can be obtained not only through the fission of massive atoms, but also through the union of two light atomic nuclei into a somewhat heavier one (*nuclear fusion*). In particular, colossal energies can be obtained if hydrogen nuclei are fused to helium.

In order to force hydrogen atoms together, past the shielding of the electron which circles the nucleus, tremendous energies must be given them. Such energies are attained in the centers of the sun and of other stars. The radiation of the sun (reaching the earth in undiminished quantities for billions of years) is the energy produced by the nuclear fusion of millions of tons of hydrogen every second.

In the 1950s the necessary energy could also be reached by exploding a fission bomb, and methods were devised for using a fission bomb to spark off a still greater and more destructive variety of nuclear bomb. The result was what is variously called a "hydrogen bomb," an "H-bomb," a "thermonuclear device" but, most properly, a *fusion bomb*.

Fusion bombs have been constructed and exploded with thousands of times the destructive potential of the first fission bombs that destroyed two cities in Japan. A single large fusion bomb could destroy utterly even the greatest city, and if all the fusion bombs now existing were exploded over various cities, it is possible that all life would be destroyed by direct blast and fire, and by scattered radioactivity (*fallout*).

Even the fusion bomb, however, may have uses above and beyond destruction. Among the most important experimental work being conducted at the present time is the attempt to produce extremely high temperatures of hundreds of millions of degrees in a controlled fashion (and not in the center of an exploding fission bomb) and to maintain those temperatures long enough to spark a fusion reaction.

If such a fusion reaction can then be kept going at a controlled rate, fantastic quantities of energy may be produced. The fuel would be deuterium, or heavy hydrogen, which is present in tremendous quantities in the oceans—quantities vast enough to last us for millions of years.

Never before has mankind had to face the possibility of extinction in an all-out fusion bomb war, nor has it had occasion for hope of unexampled prosperity in the taming of that same fusion bomb.

Either fate could result from a single branch of scientific advance.

We are gaining the knowledge; science is giving us that.

Now we need wisdom as well.

INDEX

SCIENCE STUDY SERIES

BATTAN, LOUIS J. *The Nature of Violent Storms,* S19
Radar Observes the Weather, S24
Cloud Physics and Cloud Seeding, S29

BENADE, ARTHUR H. *Horns, Strings & Harmony,* S11

BITTER, FRANCIS *Magnets: The Education of a Physicist,* S2
Mathematical Aspects of Physics: An Introduction, S32

BONDI, HERMANN *The Universe at Large,* S14

BOYS, SIR CHARLES VERNON *Soap Bubbles and the Forces Which Mould Them,* S3

BROWN, SANBORN C. *Count Rumford,* S28

COHEN, I. BERNARD *The Birth of a New Physics,* S10

DAVIS, KENNETH S., & DAY, JOHN ARTHUR *Water: The Mirror of Science,* S18

DUBOS, RENE *Pasteur and Modern Science,* S15

FINK, DONALD G., & LUTYENS, DAVID M. *The Physics of Television,* S8

GALAMBOS, ROBERT *Nerves and Muscles,* S25

GAMOW, GEORGE *Gravity,* S22

GRIFFIN, DONALD R. *Echoes of Bats and Men,* S4

HOLDEN, ALAN, & SINGER, PHYLIS *Crystals and Crystal Growing,* S7

HUGHES, DONALD J. *The Neutron Story,* S1

HURLEY, PATRICK M. *How Old Is the Earth?* S5

JAFFE, BERNARD *Michelson and the Speed of Light,* S13

KOESTLER, ARTHUR *The Watershed: A Biography of Johannes Kepler,* S16

LITTAUER, RAPHAEL, & WILSON, ROBERT R. *Accelerators: Machines of Nuclear Physics,* S17

MACDONALD, D. K. C. *Near Zero: The Physics of Low Temperature,* S20

OVENDEN, MICHAEL W. *Life in the Universe,* S23

PAGE, ROBERT MORRIS *The Origin of Radar,* S26

ROMER, ALFRED *The Restless Atom,* S12

SANDFORT, JOHN F. *Heat Engines,* S27

SHAPIRO, ASCHER H. *Shape and Flow: The Fluid Dynamics of Drag,* S21

VAN BERGEIJK, WILLEM A.; PIERCE, JOHN R.; & DAVID, EDWARD E., JR. *Waves and the Ear,* S9

WEAVER, WARREN *Lady Luck: The Theory of Probability,* S30

WEISSKOPF, VICTOR F. *Knowledge and Wonder: The Natural World as Man Knows It,* S31